SCENES FOR TEENAGERS

Edited and adapted by Shaun McKenna

OBERON BOOKS
LONDON

First published by Oberon Books Ltd. (incorporating Absolute Classics) in 1998 in association with the London Academy of Music and Dramatic Art.

British Library Cataloguing-in-Publication Data
A catalogue record for this book is available from the British Library.

ISBN 1 84002 031 8

Cover design: Andrzej Klimowski

Typography: Richard Doust

Printed in Great Britain by Arrowhead Books Ltd., Reading.

INTRODUCTION

This is a collection of original and adapted scenes suitable for 13 – 18 year olds. Some scenes are taken from my own theatre and radio plays and adaptations. I have adapted others expressly for this collection, from a range of classic and contemporary novels. These are credited as being by the author of the novel. Some of the scenes are from familiar and popular sources. However, the characters and scenes themselves have been chosen for their lack of familiarity.

All the selections are suitable for LAMDA examinations – though it should be borne in mind that the adapted scenes from nineteenth-century novels do not count as 'pre-1914' scenes for Acting Medals. The source material may be 'pre-1914' but the adaptation is not.

Some adapted scenes are very faithful to the dialogue in the books from which they are taken. Other scenes are more freely adapted and take more liberties with the novelist's original dialogue. Novelist's dialogue is not the same as dramatist's dialogue and often seems bald and unconvincing without the surrounding prose.

The Old Curiosity Shop has been contributed by Jean Howell, who is given full credit in the text. In the case of writers who lived beyond 1920 all the necessary copyright clearances have been obtained.

The collection is divided into two sections – Solo Scenes and Duologue Scenes. There is a reasonable choice of duologues in each possible male/female combination.

Though the material is aimed at teenagers, the characters included are by no means always in that age-range. Teenage actors need to stretch themselves and to explore physical and psychological aspects of character every bit as much as adult actors. Some of the material included here is strong and powerfully dramatic. Teachers will find that it is appropriate only for the older teenager. However, my experience as an examiner reinforces my belief that all the characters contained in this collection should be within reach for the young performer at some point during their teenage years.

Shaun McKenna

CONTENTS

SOLO SCENES

DUOLOGUE SCENES

SOLO SCENES

EIGHT COUSINS,
or THE AUNT HILL

by Louisa May Alcott

ROSE is 14, an orphan girl from New England who has gone to live in the Southern States of America with her mother's family. She finds herself surrounded by a great many aunts and cousins. She is speaking to her guardian, the eccentric but kindly UNCLE ALEC. The novel was written, and is set, in the 1870s.

ROSE: I'm sorry I was cross, uncle, when I ought to thank you for taking so much interest in me. I guess you are right about being thorough and studying the 'three Rs.' I used to understand a great deal better when papa taught me just a few lessons than when Miss Power hurried me through so many. I declare my head used to be a jumble of French and German, history and arithmetic, grammar and music – I used to feel sometimes as though it was about to split.

Thank you for my pocket money. Uncle Mac gave me an account book when I went to school and I used to put down my expenses, but I couldn't make them go very well. Figures are one thing I'm not a bit clever about. I do hate sums! Uncle, when you add up your expenses do you ever find you have got more money than you had in the beginning? I do. Papa used to say he found exactly the opposite. It's very curious but I can never make things come out square. If I've got to keep accounts, you had better teach me how to do it. I must begin in the right way even if it all goes wrong afterwards. Please don't laugh! I know I'm very stupid and my book is a disgrace, but all those numbers just seem to run away with me. The dollars and the cents get all mixed. Perhaps if I could straighten them out a little... You like sailing, uncle. Can you show me how to make them ship-shape?

Oh, and... I hate to ask, but... could I borrow ninepence?

THE OLD CURIOSITY SHOP

by Charles Dickens
adapted by Jean Howell

NELL, a young, unsophisticated, sincere orphan girl, is being brought up in poverty by a devoted grandfather who works unsparingly for her well-being. In this speech, LITTLE NELL confides about her grandfather to sympathetic MRS QUILP. NELL does not know that the conversation is being overheard by MRS QUILP's unscrupulous husband.

LITTLE NELL: I used to read to him by the fireside, and he sat listening, and when I stopped and we began to talk, he told me about my mother, and how she once looked and spoke just like me when she was a little child. Then he used to take me on his knee and try to make me understand that she was not lying in her grave, but had flown to a beautiful country beyond the sky where nothing ever died or grew old – we were very happy once.

I cry very seldom – but I have kept this to myself for a long time and I am not quite well, I think, for the tears come into my eyes and I cannot keep them back. I don't mind telling you my grief, for I know you will not tell it to any one again.

We often walked in the fields and among the green trees, and when we came home at night we liked it better for being tired and said what a happy place it was. And if it was dark and rather dull we used to say, what did it matter to us, for it only made us remember our last walk with greater pleasure and look forward to our next one. But now we never have those walks and though it is the same house it is darker and much more gloomy than it used to be, indeed.

Mind you, don't suppose that grandfather is less kind to me than he was. I think he loves me better every day and is kinder and more affectionate than he was the day before. You do not know how fond he is of me. I am sure he loves me dearly, as dearly as I love him. But I have not told you the greatest change of all, and this you must never breathe again to any one. He has no sleep or rest but that which he takes by day in his easy chair; for every night, and almost all night long, he is away from home. When he comes home in the morning, which is generally just before day, I let him in. Last night he was very late and it was quite light. I saw that his face was deadly pale, that his eyes were bloodshot, and that his legs trembled as he walked. When I had gone to bed again, I heard him groan. I got up and ran back to him and heard him say, before he knew that I was there, that he could not bear his life much longer and if it were not for the child, would wish to die. What shall I do?

Oh, what shall I do?

TO SERVE THEM ALL MY DAYS

by R.F. Delderfield
dramatised by Shaun McKenna

This dramatisation of Delderfield's famous novel was premiered at the Royal Theatre, Northampton in 1992 and is soon to be published by Oberon Books.

JULIA DARBYSHIRE is a young woman, believed to be a widow, who has come to teach at an isolated private boy's school. It is 1919. A boy, KEITH BLADES, has become romantically attached to her and she has been unable to prevent herself from returning his feelings. Another teacher, MR POWLETT-JONES, has discovered what is going on and has spoken to her tactfully.

JULIA: You say your wife advised you to come to me. Does that mean you don't intend to make it public? Oh, we haven't been lovers. You can set your mind at rest on that count. We haven't been and we wouldn't have been. On my honour, if that's worth anything to you. The boy has enough problems, without becoming involved with his teacher.

You're handling this very nicely. I shouldn't be ungrateful.

Pause.

He wrote me a poem. It was rather good, a pastiche of Herrick. 'When as in silks my Julia goes.' That's my name. Julia. Did you know? He had problems, he needed someone to talk to. It would have been callous not to listen, to try to... comfort. You'll say I carried comfort a little far. I've no excuse. I know that.

You were in the war, weren't you? (*Taking a photograph from her bag.*) This was my husband. I say "was" because he's just as dead as the million others in France even though I'm still married to him. We had one week together before he was posted. What's left of him is at the military hospital at Netley and likely to stay there as long as the government persists in regarding euthanasia as a crime, not a duty. I'm sorry if I'm embarrassing you but... Keith was the first person since I came here – no, since I saw that thing they said was my husband – who talked to me. Really talked. To me.

I'll resign, of course. I'll tell Keith there's good news from the hospital, that I have to go to my husband. He's still young enough to believe in the nobility of self-sacrifice. And please... don't worry about me. I'll survive. One always does, don't you find?

THE MOONSTONE

by Wilkie Collins

This Victorian novel has been labeled the first detective novel. The beautiful young LADY RACHEL VERRINDER has inherited a huge yellow diamond, known as 'The Moonstone' from her deceased uncle. Now the diamond has been stolen. RACHEL is talking to her mother's steward, GABRIEL BETTEREDGE.

RACHEL: Sergeant Cuff? Must I see him? Can't you represent me, Gabriel? I'm afraid my nerves are a little shaken. There is something about that police-officer from London which I recoil from – I don't know why. I feel he is bringing nothing but trouble and misery into the house. I'm sure I'm being entirely foolish – but I cannot shake the feeling. It is unlike me, I know, but after that incident downstairs... (*Laughing.*) Fancy accusing me of stealing my own diamond. He is supposed to be the best detective in England and he pursues such an idea as that! Ask him what he thinks and he will declare that I have sold the Moonstone to pay my private debts! As if I had such debts! Then he accuses Godfrey, dear, kind Godfrey. The whole situation would be laughable if it were not so serious. To accuse a man who is obviously innocent! I declare I think I should go straight to a magistrate. Let Godfrey swear to his innocence on paper and I will sign it to show my support and faith in him. If he will not, for modesty's sake, why! I will write to the newspapers myself. I'll go out and cry it in the streets. Godfrey is a braver, truer friend than I have ever given him credit for. Up till now, I have not thought as highly of him as I should. And now I must endure the odious Sergeant Cuff again, here, in my own drawing room.

Well, if I must, I must. But I shan't see him alone. Bring him in, Gabriel, and stay as long as he stays.

THERESE RAQUIN

by Emile Zola

THERESE RAQUIN, a young woman, has murdered her husband in collusion with her lover, LAURENT. MADAME RAQUIN, her mother-in-law, has suffered a severe stroke as a result and is now paralysed. THERESE confesses to the immobile, distressed MADAME RAQUIN, whilst trying to feed her.

THERESE: I can't let you die till you've forgiven me. And you will forgive me, sooner or later, I know you will. I'm a terrible person and I don't deserve it, but I need it. I deceived you. I let him kill Camille. I didn't know he was going to, not until it was too late. And then I was scared he'd kill me too.

I know what it felt like for Camille. I know every detail. He thought Laurent was messing about, that it was a game, until he saw his eyes. That's why he bit him. He couldn't force him off so he clawed and scratched, like a cat when you stuff it in a sack with a brick. Cats know when their number's up.

Then he was in the water and the panic started. He kept getting mouthfuls of slime, he retched, he couldn't keep his head up. And all the time Laurent kept smashing the oar down on his head. He saw all these colours, pretty colours, and he thought his heart was going to burst out through his ribs and all he knew about was how much he hurt. Then the weeds clutched at his heels and he was being dragged down and down... He tried to scream but his lungs filled up with filth and then he was dead. That was better. It was cool and dark and quiet and there was no pain any more. But after a bit his body began to feel tight. His flesh was swelling in the water. It was uncomfortable, like when you eat too much hot bread.

The pain really started then. He itched. But it wasn't really itching, he realised that after an hour or two. He was being eaten. All the little fishes had come for their dinner. So many tiny mouths, nibbling at him. They ate the soft parts first. His flesh got spongier and spongier and soon there were so many fishes he couldn't think up names for them all any more.

Then he was dragged up and squeezed out and laid on a slab in the morgue, like a herring. That's where Laurent saw him. Camille was pleased about that. He wanted Laurent to know what it had been like. He wanted me to know, too, but I wasn't brave enough to go to the morgue. That's why he started coming to me in the night.

Silly boy. He didn't have to tell me how it felt. I already knew. I've been drowning too.

I know you forgive me. I can see the tears in your eyes.

HOW GREEN WAS MY VALLEY

by Richard Llewellyn
dramatised by Shaun McKenna

This adaptation of the famous novel of life at the turn of the nineteenth century in a South Wales mining town was first produced at the Royal Theatre, Northampton in 1990. BETH MORGAN is a miner's wife, fiercely protective of her family. In a strike brewing at the colliery her son DAVY has become a radical activist. As a result, MORGAN, DAVY's father and BETH's husband, has been vilified by some of his fellow workers. At a meeting high in the mountains, late at night, BETH pushes herself forward.

BETH: Let me speak, now. I will speak! I am Beth Morgan and I have come up here tonight because I hear you are talking against my husband. Two things in this world I do hate. One is talking behind the back and the other is lice. So you should know what I think of you. You are all a lot of cowards to talk against my husband. He has done nothing against you, and never would, and you know it well. He is Superintendent of the colliery now because every man will have his reward for working, and that is his. For you to think that he is with the owners because he has had his reward is not only nonsense but downright wickedness. How some of you can sit in the same Chapel with him I cannot tell. But this I will tell you. If harm do come to my Gwilym, I will find out the men and I will kill them with my hands. That I swear by God Almighty. And there will be no Hell for me. Nobody will go to Hell for killing lice.

Hush, Davy, do not speak to me. I am not your mother when you are with these. You are lice like them. And if your father comes to harm... you will be the first to go.

JANE EYRE

by Charlotte Bronte
dramatised by Shaun McKenna

This dramatisation of Charlotte Bronte's famous novel was first performed at St Paul's Girls School in 1988. Written for a large number of girls, it was an opportunity to explore some of the less central female characters. ELIZA REED finally tells her spoiled sister, GEORGIANA, exactly what she thinks of her.

ELIZA: Georgiana, a more vain and absurd creature than you never walked the earth! I swear you had no right to be born, for you make no use of being alive! Instead of living for, in, with yourself as any reasonable person would, all you want to do is fasten your feebleness around someone else's neck. If you can find nobody willing to take you on – fat, weak, puffy, useless thing that you are – you wail and cry about how neglected and miserable you are. You can't settle in any one place – you always want excitement, travel, new faces around you, new clothes to adorn you. You must be admired, you must be flattered, you must be courted. You must have music, you must have dancing, you must have society! Haven't you the sense to devise a system for yourself which will make you independent? Which will put you in charge of your own destiny? Take one day. Divide it into sections, give each section its appointed task, leave yourself no spare quarters of an hour in which you might be melancholy, no ten minutes, no five minutes spare. Do each piece of business in turn with method, with rigid regularity. You will find the day has drawn to a close almost before it has begun – you have had no time to be unhappy and have depended on nobody else. Start tomorrow, Georgiana, that's my advice – and it is the only advice I shall ever offer you.

If you neglect to take it – and it is your right to refuse to take it – then let me tell you this: after mother's death I shall wash my hands of you. From the day her coffin is carried to Gateshead church you and I will be as separate as if we had never known each other. Don't think that just because we shared the same parents I shall acknowledge that you have any claim on me. If the whole human race were swept away and only the two of us stood on this earth, I should turn my back on you and walk away.

TESS OF THE D'URBEVILLES

by Thomas Hardy

TESS, a young country girl, has been seduced and made pregnant by ALEC D'URBEVILLE. She subsequently finds true love with ANGEL CLARE, a very moral young man, but for a long time has to keep her illegitimate child a secret. Then – just as things finally seem to be going well for TESS, D'URBEVILLE reappears in her life and she kills him. The action in set in nineteenth century 'Wessex'. Here, TESS tells ANGEL what she has done.

TESS: (*Pale and breathless.*) I have done it. I have killed him, I don't know how. Still, I owed it to you, and to myself, Angel. I feared long ago, when I struck him on the mouth with my glove, that I might do it someday. He trapped me when I was too young to know better. He has wronged me – and you, Angel, through me. He has come between us and ruined us. He can't do that any more. I never loved him as I love you. You do know that, don't you? You left me and didn't come back. What was I to do? I had to go back to him. Why did you leave me? Don't you know how much I love you? I don't blame you, but... I killed him so that you might forgive my sin against you. You will forgive me, won't you, now I have proved my love? It came to me like a shining light that this was the way I could get you back. I can't bear to be without you – you've no idea how entirely I was unable to bear you not loving me. Say you love me, Angel. Say you love me.

He heard me crying about you and he said terrible things to me. He called you a foul name and then I did it. I could not bear it. He had nagged me about you before. Then I dressed myself and came away to find you. You do love me, don't you, Angel? You do forgive me?

DAISY MILLER

by Henry James

This short novel is set in Italy, among Americans undertaking 'the Grand Tour' in the late nineteenth century. DAISY MILLER is a beautiful, charming, captivating and utterly infuriating eighteen year old American girl who makes the life of the besotted MR WINTERBOURNE hell.

DAISY: Why haven't you been to see me, Mr Winterbourne? You can't get out of that. Oh, you say you have only just stepped out of the train but you have had time to go and see Mrs Walker. Do you prefer Mrs Walker's company to mine?

Oh, I know where you knew her. You knew her at Geneva. She told me so. Well, you knew me at Vevey. That's just as good. So you ought to have come. We've got splendid rooms at the hotel; Eugenio says they're the best rooms in Rome. We are going to stay all winter, if we don't die of the fever; and if we do, I guess we'll stay longer! (*Laughs.*) It's a great deal nicer than I thought. I thought it would be fearfully quiet and dreadfully poky. I was sure we would be going round all the time with one of those dreadful old men that explain about the pictures and things. But we only had about a week of that and now I'm enjoying myself. I know ever so many people and they are all charming. The society's extremely select. There are all kinds – English and Germans and Italians. I think I like the English best, I like their style of conversation. There's something or other every day. There's not much dancing – but then I never felt dancing was everything. I was always fond of conversation. I guess I shall have plenty at Mrs Walker's, her rooms are so small. And of course, dear Mr Winterbourne, we can talk about you.

Are you sorry now you didn't come to see me straight away? I hope you are sorry. Don't imagine I have missed you, though, for as you can see, I have been thoroughly busy.

JANE EYRE

by Charlotte Bronte
dramatised by Shaun McKenna

See note on the dramatisation on page 18. This soliloquy closed the first act. JANE EYRE, an 18 year old governess, has started to fall in love with her employer, EDWARD ROCHESTER. Having just saved him from a fire, she is surprised the next morning to find he has left the house – and distressed to learn that he has gone to visit the beautiful BLANCHE INGRAM, whom he is expected to marry.

JANE: You? A favourite with Mr Rochester? You – gifted with the power of pleasing him? You – important to him in any way? You are a fool, Jane Eyre. You have taken pleasure in casual exchanges between a master and his dependent. How could you dare? How could you have been so presumptuous? Where is your self-control now? Look at yourself, Jane Eyre. What good will it do you to be flattered by your superior? What madness is it in any woman to let a secret love kindle within her when it can only lead, like a marsh-light, to a muddy wilderness from whence there can be no return?

Listen to your sentence then, Jane Eyre. Tomorrow put your glass before you and draw what you see, faithfully, without softening one defect. Omit no harsh line, no blemish. And underneath it write, 'Portrait of a governess, poor and plain'. Then take a piece of smooth ivory, mix your freshest, clearest tints, choose your most delicate brushes and create the loveliest face you can imagine. Remember every detail of Mrs Fairfax's description of Miss Ingram and call it, 'Blanche, an accomplished lady of rank'. And whenever, in the future, you should be weak enough to fancy Mr Rochester thinks well of you, take out the two portraits and compare them.

What did you say, Mr Rochester? 'I have never felt jealousy because I have never loved?' Well, sir, I feel jealousy now. My soul no longer sleeps.

THE POSTMAN ALWAYS RINGS TWICE

by James M. Cain
dramatised by Shaun McKenna

This is taken from a radio adaptation of Cain's classic 'noir' thriller, broadcast on Radio Four in 1992. It is set in Southern California in the early 1930s. CORA PAPADAKIS is unhappily married to a Greek lunch-room owner and has started an affair with FRANK CHAMBERS, an itinerant worker, who is helping out her husband. CORA is young but already fading.

CORA: Why did I marry him? You spend two years in a Los Angeles hash house, you'll marry the first guy you meet with a gold watch. I never told you 'bout the hash house, did I? I never told you anything. Guess we didn't waste time talking. You don't know anything about me.

(*Laughing.*) Hey, that tickles! Keep your hands to yourself.

Three years ago I won a beauty contest, a dopey high school beauty contest in Des Moines. The prize was a trip to Hollywood. I got off the Chief with fifteen guys taking my picture. Then the screen test. Two weeks later I was in the hash house. That screen test – it was part of the prize. It was alright in the face. But they talk now, the pictures. And as soon as I started to talk up there on the screen, they knew. And so did I. I had about as much chance in pictures as a monkey. Not as much. A monkey can make you laugh. I couldn't go home and give them the satisfaction, so it was the hash house. Two years of guys pinching your leg and leaving nickel tips and asking how about a little party tonight. I went on some of them parties, Frank. You know what I mean about them parties?

Then Nick came along. I took him and, so help me,
I meant to stick by him, Frank. But I can't. Not any
more. He calls me his 'little white bird' – you've heard
him. God, do I look like a little white bird?

BLEAK HOUSE

by Charles Dickens

Young ADA and her cousin RICHARD have been engaged for years in a hopeless Chancery suit about their family inheritance. It has finally sent RICHARD off the rails. ADA has married him to try to prevent the crash. Here she confides in her cousin, ESTHER.

ADA: Esther, my dearest, I want to be a good wife, a very, very good wife. When I married Richard I was not unaware of what lay before us. I had been very happy for a long time with you and I had never known any trouble or anxiety. You had looked after me so well, Esther. But I did understand the danger he was in. I thought... Oh, I thought that if we were married I could convince him that he was making a mistake; that he might come to regard this wretched Chancery suit in a new way as my husband – but no, he pursues it all the more desperately. But – and I want you to understand this – even if I had not had the hope that I could change him, I would still have married him. Does that make any sense to you? Don't think that I can't see what you see and fear what you fear. Nobody can understand him better than I do. I see him at his worst, every day. I watch him in his sleep. I know every change of his face. But I made up my mind, when we married, that I would never show him I grieved for what he did – that would make him more unhappy. He loves me and is gentle towards me. When he comes home at night, in despair as he sometimes is, I want him to find no trouble in my face. I want him to see what it is he loved in me. I married him to do this, and it supports me.

Something else supports me too. I look forward a little way and think how he might change if we were to have a child. That might redeem him. But whenever I think of that I grow frightened. When I look in his face, I grow frightened. I fear he may not live long enough to see his child.

MADDIE

by Shaun McKenna,
Steven Dexter and Stephen Keeling

This musical comedy premiered at Salisbury in 1996 and
opened in the West End in the autumn of 1997. It concerns
the ghost of MADDIE, a 1920s flapper, who possesses the
body of JAN, wife of NICK CHEYNEY. NICK has fallen in
love with MADDIE in his wife's body. Just as JAN was about
to realise what had happened to her, MADDIE re-possesses
her body. MADDIE is a bundle of energy. The show is set in
San Francisco in 1981.

MADDIE: Hi, sheik! (*With a whoop.*) Boy, oh boy. Don't
worry, she's gone for now. Oh Nicky, it's so good to love
again. Thank you, Jan.

What do you mean, 'why?' She was in my room. She
touched my message. That's how I got through. She
wanted to know how it felt to be me. Whoo! I was so
lucky. All those forces, all at once. My movie, in my
room. My message on the wall. Jan. And, of course,
you. Yes, you. You fell in love with me at first sight.

Oh, Nicky, don't be stuffy. That gave me the extra kick
I needed. All that lovely energy. OK, so her hair's a
stupid colour. And skinny arms. Not bad legs, I must
say, though mine were better. The inside of her mouth
feels kinda funny. But fine for kissing, eh Nicky?

She kisses him.

Whoo! That's better. Let's carry on where we left off.

She puts a record on the gramophone.

The 'Frisco Flip!

Now, if Jan really does work it out... say you didn't know.
(*Imitating NICK.*) 'Madeline Marsh? I had no idea.'

C'mon and dance.

THE WOMAN IN WHITE

by Wilkie Collins

LAURA, a pretty young heiress, is betrothed to the sinister
Sir Percival Glyde, a man much her senior. She has fallen in
love with another man. A mystery surrounds Glyde and
Laura has been forced to alter her will – much to her distress
and consternation. Here she confides in her cousin, Marian.
The period is the 1880s.

LAURA: I can never claim my release from the engagement.
Whatever happens, it must all end miserably for me.
All I can do, Marian, is not to add the remembrance that
I have broken my promise and forgotten my father's
dying words, to make that wretchedness worse. All I can
do is tell Sir Percival everything – the truth, with my own
lips – and let him release me, if he will, not because I ask
him but because he knows everything.

Can I tell him I am opposed to the marriage, when the
engagement was made for me by my father, with my
own consent? I should have kept my promise – not
happily, I am afraid, but still contentedly. I should have
kept my engagement if I had not allowed another love to
grow in my heart, which was not there when I promised
to be Sir Percival's wife. He has a right to know I love
somebody else. I shall not lower myself by gaining my
release with a lie. I cannot lie to him, Marian. Better Sir
Percival should doubt my motives and misjudge my
conduct if he will than I should first be false to him in
thought and then mean enough to serve my own interests
by hiding the falsehood.

Don't be angry with me, Marian. I have thought about
little else for days. I can be brave, I'm sure of it, when
my own conscience tells me I am right. But... will you be
with me tomorrow when I speak to him? I will say

nothing wrong, nothing that you or I need be ashamed of, but – oh, I shall be so relieved to get this done with. And I would like to know that you are there with me, in case I falter. Will you?

EIGHT COUSINS
or THE AUNT HILL

by Louisa May Alcott

ARCHIE is 14 and one of the boisterous American cousins of young ROSE, recently orphaned. ROSE has come to live with her father's relatives. She is spending the day with her cousins on an island, where they have set up camp. The novel was written, and is set, in the 1870s.

ARCHIE: Hello, Rose! What are you doing here so early? You were not supposed to come until this afternoon, when Mamma would be here to receive you. Everything is in a mess here now – oh, except your tent. We got that ready first, so you can sit in there and watch us work, if you've a mind to. Mind that washing line! We had a jolly good swim before dinner and I told the Brats – that's your cousin Jamie and cousin John – to hang their things up to dry. I hope you brought your swimming things, Rose. You're one of us now, and you can have no end of fun learning to dive and float and tread water.

(*Calling to his companions.*) Come on, you lazy lubbers! Fall to work or we won't be ready before Mamma gets here. Mac and Steve, bring up the rest of the straw. Prince, take Rose to her tent! And if you two have finished eating, you can clear the table. (*To ROSE.*) We always camp out somewhere during the summer vacation. We thought we'd try this Island for a change. We have fireworks and all sorts of larks. We big fellows often camp for a week but this year the small chaps wanted to come, so we let them. We have a cave, and we can play Captain Kidd and the pirates and have shipwrecks and races and all sorts of games. Of course, Charlie and I are rather grown-up for that sort of thing, but we do it to please the children. I'm going to fry fish and make chowder for luncheon. Shall I show you how to do it, or do you want to go to your tent? You want to help? Oh, that's grand!

LE GRAND MEAULNES

by Alain-Fournier

AUGUSTIN MEAULNES, a charismatic 15 year old schoolboy, has taken a cart and gone off on an adventure. On his return to school, a week later, he is silent about where he has been – until he finally tells his only friend, FRANÇOIS SEUREL. A new stage adaptation by Shaun McKenna of this famous French novel, entitled *The Great Adventure*, is soon to be published by Oberon Books.

MEAULNES: I haven't told anyone what happened because they won't believe me. I don't care if I'm punished for playing truant, that doesn't matter, but... It was a bit of a lark, that's all. I saw the pony and trap, it was a beautiful day, and I thought... to hell with History and Latin and Algebra. And off I rode. It was great. I went off towards the sun. I must have fallen asleep on the trap because when I woke up it was evening, and I didn't know where I was – I didn't even recognise the lie of the land. The pony must have been straying for hours. I begged some bread and cheese from a farmer's wife. She pointed me towards a village. I didn't recognise the name but I thought, if I go there, there'll be a signpost, or someone else to ask or... Anyway, it wouldn't kill me to spend a night under the trees.

The pony was ambling along, stopping to eat grass. The sky was violet – it was really beautiful, a magical evening. And then, in the distance, I heard... You won't believe me. I heard music, soft, rippling, beautiful music, like something in a dream. I got down from the trap. The music was coming from the woods. I went into the woods. Deeper and deeper, the music was getting louder but still so sweet, so enchanting. A glimmer of light in the distance. Then another, and another. Blue lights, green lights, white lights, pink lights. And music. And laughter now – I could hear people laughing on the other side of the trees.

Of course I walked on. I came to the edge of the woods and there it was. A festival. A beautiful château, with lanterns strung all around it, music playing, men dancing with beautiful ladies, boys rolling hoops, everything you could imagine. Then someone came up with a tray and offered me a pastry – it was the softest, sweetest pastry I've ever tasted. Like something you might taste in a fairy tale. And it felt so right to be there.

You believe me, François, don't you?

THE SILVER CHAIR

by C.S. Lewis

PUDDLEGLUM is a Marsh-wiggle in the strange land of Narnia. He has met JILL and EUSTACE who are seeking to free PRINCE RILIAN from the enchantment of his silver chair. They enlist his help. PUDDLEGLUM is as gloomy as his name suggests.

PUDDLEGLUM: Can I help you to find Prince Rilian? Well, I don't know that you'd call it help. I don't know that anyone can actually help. It stands to reason we're not likely to get very far on a journey to the North, not at this time of year, with the winter coming on soon and all. And an early winter, too, by the look of things. But you mustn't let that make you down-hearted. Very likely, what with enemies, and mountains, and rivers to cross, and losing our way, and next to nothing to eat, and sore feet, we'll hardly notice the weather. And if we don't get far enough to do any good, we may get far enough not to get back in a hurry. Oh, I'm coming with you, of course. Might as well, you see. I don't suppose we shall ever see the King back in Narnia, now that he's once set off for foreign parts; and he had a nasty cough when he left. And you'll find there'll have been a bad harvest after this terribly dry summer. And I shouldn't wonder if some enemy attacked us. Mark my words.

All the others who ever went looking for Prince Rilian started from that same fountain where the Lord Drinian saw the lady. They went north, mostly. And as none of them ever came back, we can't say exactly how they got on. You say Aslan told you to start by finding a Ruined City of giants? I won't say I haven't heard of that Ruined City. You wouldn't start from that fountain, though. You'd have to go across Ettinsmoor. Look over there, northward. See those hills and bits of cliff? That's the

beginning of Ettinsmoor. But there's a river between it
and us; the river Shribble. No bridges, of course. And
you're right, you'll meet people on Ettinsmoor. People.
It's not for me to say they aren't alright in their own way.
If you like their way. They're giants.

Adapted from The Silver Chair © C.S. Lewis plc Ltd. 1953 by
permission of C.S. Lewis plc Ltd.

HOW GREEN WAS MY VALLEY

by Richard Llewellyn
dramatised by Shaun McKenna

See note on the play on page 17. 17 year old HUW MORGAN describes his father's last moments of life, after he is caught in a landslide in a coal mine.

HUW: Up against the coal face he was, where the rock had not filled. His head was on a pillow of rock and sheets and bedclothes of rock covered him to the neck. And I saw that if I moved only one bit, the roof would fall in. I was afraid to put my hands with tenderness on him for fear my touch might be an extra hurt.

We dig in the Earth and hurt her with our tunnels and shafts. But the Earth has patience with us. As long as we put back the flesh we have taken and make strong what we have weakened. But if we do not – and the owners have not – she waits, and when she finds us, she bears down and makes us a part of her, flesh of her flesh, with our clay in place of the clay we have so thoughtlessly shoveled away. And so she bore down on Dada.

But as the blood ran from his mouth and nose, and the redness ran from his eyes, I saw the shining smile in them, that came from a brightness inside him. And I was filled with bitter pride that he was my father, fighting still and unafraid.

And so he smiled, and went.

God could have had him a hundred ways. But He chose to have him like that. He went easy, Mama.

RULING PASSIONS

by Shaun McKenna

RULING PASSIONS is a psychological drama based on a nineteenth century French murder case. It was premiered at the Royal Theatre, Northampton in 1994. GABRIEL PASQUIER is Chancellor of France. He is a vain, elderly dandy with an affected manner that hides a sophisticated and intelligent mind. He is investigating the murder of the DUCHESSE DE PRASLIN and is interviewing the family governess, HENRIETTE DELUZY, whom he believes can be made to admit her guilt.

PASQUIER: Mademoiselle Deluzy, I am investigating a murder not writing a ten centime novelette. You expect me to believe that the head of one of the oldest Catholic families in France, a Privy Counsellor married to a great military fortune formed a purely platonic attachment to a lubricious governess with a sentimental turn of phrase?

You had an affair. You turned the children against their mother. You became his mistress. When it became a public scandal you were dismissed without a reference. All that lay ahead for you, mademoiselle, was the gutter. So one night, you entered the house and brutally slaughtered your rival. The rest is romantic taradiddle, born of delusion and ambition. Did you expect him to marry you? You say you would do nothing to hurt the children – yet you murdered their mother.

(*Producing papers.*) There were eleven wounds on her head, five of them deep and large. The skull was fractured in four places, the blows having been dealt from behind with a sharp weapon. You stood behind her as you stabbed, then. There were gashes to the nose, the left eye, the lower lip and the chin where the marks of fingernails are clearly to be seen. If you can see anything through the blood.

Four large wounds were made in her neck, though neither the carotid artery nor inner jugular vein were severed, thus ensuring a slow and painful death. On the hands, chest and abdomen there were another ten wounds, of varying depth. The thumb of the left hand was nearly severed at the joint. There were also some forty odd bruises and livid marks about her body. The number and situations of the wounds attest that her death was preceded by a long and violent struggle.

He pauses for breath.

A man was seen leaving the gardens on the Champs Elysées side, shortly before five a.m. A man. Or a woman in man's clothing. Your neighbour at the lodging house cannot give you an alibi. Your motive is clear. The Duc is a wealthy, fascinating man. The Duchesse was your rival in love and in the affections of her children. You have condemned yourself out of your own mouth. Confess.

THERESE RAQUIN

by Emile Zola

LAURENT has plotted with THERESE to murder her husband, CAMILLE RAQUIN, by staging a drowning accident. Now it is imperative that he maintains the illusion of his innocence. The body of CAMILLE has been found in the Seine, after floating down-river. Here, LAURENT tells a family friend of his visit to the Morgue.

LAURENT: Michaud, I've... I've seen him. I've seen Raquin. In the Morgue. I... I saw him.

I've been going there every day. I had to. I had to know that – that he was dead, you see. (*Violently.*) It's a circus in there. I was sick the first day. But I couldn't get it out of my head, couldn't stop going there. There are regulars, you know. There's been this woman, this smart woman, in a grey silk skirt. She smells of roses. Beautiful hands. I watched her.

Don't stop me. I have to talk about it. Have you ever seen a man who's been in the water a fortnight? I never knew they swelled up like that. I've never thought about it. I was looking at a... a man. He was, I don't know, sort of – yellowish. Muddy looking. Sounds stupid, eh? His flesh was so soft and rotten the running water was flaking it away. His feet were coming adrift, his collarbone was sticking out through his skin. His teeth were very white and – his tongue – the tip of his tongue – was black. There was so much pain in his eyes. They were staring right at me. I don't have to tell you who it was, do I?

I didn't realise for a bit. Then I thought, 'I did that. I turned him into that.'

There was a water jet right on his face, right by his nose. It was making a hole in his face. I watched it. Then, all of a sudden, the nose – flattened out – and the lips came away. All I could see was the teeth.

He begins to shiver uncontrollably.

Michaud, he was grinning at me!

THE POSTMAN ALWAYS RINGS TWICE

by James M. Cain
dramatised by Shaun McKenna

See note on the dramatisation on page 25. CORA
PAPADAKIS and FRANK CHAMBERS have murdered
CORA's husband, and have been arraigned for it. KATZ is
the clever, slimy, shifty lawyer who has managed to get them
off. In his confused state, FRANK has been persuaded by the
District Attorney, SACKETT, to make a formal complaint
against CORA. In revenge, CORA has implicated FRANK
by confessing to a 'policeman.' KATZ explains to FRANK
how he has manoeuvred the situation.

KATZ: This has been the greatest case I ever had. Sackett
was so sure he had you. He was crowing over dinner last
night. Why, he even bet me a hundred dollars he'd get
her condemned before lunch. I should sit down, you look
a little woozy. You didn't think I'd really let her talk to
the police, did you? Kennedy works for me. That little
document is locked up in my safe right now. All Sackett
really had was that complaint you signed. You turned
yellow, didn't you. Oh well, yellow is a colour you
figure on in murder. Sackett knew that once you testified
against her, nothing on earth would stop her ratting on
you. Unfortunately our dear D.A. hadn't calculated for
the brilliance of Katz. (*Laughing.*) You should have seen
his face when she walked out of the courtroom.

How'd I work it? I traced the Greek's insurance agent.
That new policy had nothing to do with his accident. He
was hustled into it when the agent renewed his car policy.
More important, his old policies still had a week to run.
That's the whole thing. Sackett's insurance company, the
Pacific States Accident, is on a ten thousand dollar
Personal Accident policy. A lot of money. They don't want
to pay. Clear so far?

Well, in my corner I've got a Guaranty of California ten thousand dollar public liability bond and a Rocky Mountain Fidelity public liability bond for another ten thousand. That's how much?

Yes, twenty thousand. My, you walk, you talk, you even think. No wonder Mrs Papadakis is so smitten. Listen up. If she goes down for murder, Sackett's man keeps ten grand. But if you sue for injuries sustained because of attempted murder, my two fellas have to shell out twenty grand. Nasty. So I think a little. I get the three of them in a room. My two chip in ten thousand apiece to pay off Sackett's man. My friends are happy, they've saved themselves five grand apiece. Sackett's man is happy, it hasn't cost his company a bean. Mrs Papadakis is happy, she gets ten thousand dollars. I'm happy, I get a fat fee. Life is just a bowl of cherries. So who isn't happy, Chambers?

Sackett isn't happy. His insurance guy changes his testimony on the witness stand and says he's satisfied no crime was committed. They have to reduce the murder charge to manslaughter and with Cora looking like that, who's going to convict? All those pretty tears. Six months suspended sentence and they practically apologised for that.

STRANGE MEETING

by Susan Hill

BARTON is a young officer in the trenches during World War I. He has tried to keep himself cheerful by believing that the war has some great and noble purpose, but now the horror of it all has engulfed him. He is talking to his close friend, another young officer, HILLIARD.

BARTON: It was going up into the o.p. that day. I saw eleven men killed. I suppose that doesn't seem many to you. It was to me, when there wasn't even anything in particular going on, it was a 'routine day'. Eleven men. There might have been more only I didn't see them. And there were all those bodies lying out in the shell craters and they'd been there for weeks, months – I don't know. They were all swollen and black and the flies were all over them. And I had to sit there and draw a map...

You don't need me to go on.

The worst of it all is that I haven't been able to face myself. That Private who was snipered – looking at him I could have wept and wept, he seemed to be all the men who had ever been killed, John. I remember everything about him, his face, his hair, his hands, I can remember how pale his eyelashes were and I thought of how alive he'd been, how much there had been going on inside him – blood pumping round, muscles working, brain saying do this, do that, his eyes looking at me. I thought of it all – how he'd been born, had a family, I thought of everything that had gone into making him – and it wasn't that I was afraid and putting myself in his place down there on the ground. I just wanted him alive again. It seemed the only important thing. I couldn't take it in that he'd been so alive, and then he just lay, spouting out

blood, and that was that, he was dead, nothing.
Or something. I don't know.

And I had to sit there and draw a map.

MEETING JACK

by Shaun McKenna

This original radio play was broadcast on Radio Four in 1994. It deals with an incident in the life of American writer, JACK LONDON, author of *White Fang* and *The Call of the Wild* among others. LONDON was an alcoholic and in this scene has been drinking solidly for some hours. LONDON was 29 at the time but known for his physical strength and boyish charm. It is a challenging – but rewarding – speech for a young actor.

JACK: My real father was a con-man. Bill Chaney. I should be called Jack Chaney. He was an astrologer and he gave lectures in dance halls. When my Mamma found out she was pregnant, he wanted her to get rid of... of me. She wouldn't, she wanted him to marry her. When he didn't, she tried to shoot herself. When that didn't work, she took opium. He left for Oregon. She had me.

When I found out, I was nineteen. I was trying to be a writer. Nobody wanted my stuff. I borrowed a bicycle and cycled to Portland. I found Bill Chaney drunk in a hotel room. 'Hi,' I said. 'I'm your son.' He didn't want to know. He denied it. Even if it was true, he said, who'd want a bum like me for a son? He said a lot of other pretty things. And he was right. I was a bum.

I left California. I went to the Klondike, joined the gold rush. I wanted to make my fortune, see, prove I was somebody. I got frostbite, but I didn't find any gold. I found something else. We were on Lake Tagish. The freeze was starting. Many, many wolves. As the thermometer dropped the wolves came in closer to the campfires. Night after night, a couple of feet closer. We started losing dogs to them. We had to get down to Dawson City for the winter. We didn't have much chance,

but you take the hand you're dealt. We built a boat, the
Yukon Belle. Built her in two weeks. Decided we'd take
her down through Box Canyon – through the Mane of
the White Horse Rapids. Not a boat that year had made
it though those rapids. I took the helm. We hit the white
water and I screamed.

(*Suddenly screaming.*) Aaaaah!

I was so scared. But I held on. And I kept steering. And
we made it to Dawson. It was the first time I didn't feel
like a bum. I felt like a man as we sailed in. They were
out on the quay, cheering us on. I knew it would make a
story. Back in California, it did. I called it *The Belle of the
Yukon.* The *Overland Monthly* bought it for twenty-five
dollars. It got me started as a writer. This time I went to
Portland by rail. Turned up at the hotel in my best suit,
the magazine clutched like a trophy in my hand. 'Look,
dad, look what I did.' I banged on Bill Chaney's door.
A woman opened it. A scrawny, sad little woman with
washed out eyes. 'Bill's gone away,' she said. 'He won't
be back.' On the train home, I fell into conversation with
a salesman. He didn't know me from Adam. Suddenly,
he pulled a copy of the *Overland Monthly* from his coat
and gave it to me. 'Read this,' he said. 'There's a great
story called *The Belle of the Yukon*'. You know what?
I didn't care that he liked it. There was only one person
I wanted to like it.

I expect Bill Chaney's dead by now. You see, Priddy...
Priddy?

PRIDDY is asleep. JACK pours himself a shot of bourbon.

Your health, Priddy.

DUOLOGUE SCENES

EIGHT COUSINS
or THE AUNT HILL

by Louisa May Alcott

ROSE is a 14 year old orphan, here looking after her 14 year old cousin, MAC, who has strained his eyes. MAC has been ordered by the doctor to stay in a darkened room and wear an eye-shade for the foreseeable future. It is America in the 1860s.

MAC: What's the date?

ROSE: August the seventh, I think.

MAC: That's more than half the school vacation gone and I've only had a week of it. It's too hard.

ROSE: Yes, it is hard, but there's more to come and you may be able to enjoy that.

MAC: May? I *will* be able. Does that old noodle of a doctor think I'm going to stay shut up in here much longer?

ROSE: I guess he does, unless your eyes get on faster than they have yet.

MAC: Has he said anything else?

ROSE: I haven't seen him. Shall I read to you?

MAC: No, not now. I want you to tell me something.

ROSE: What's that?

MAC: I need to know, and you've got to tell me.

ROSE: What's that?

MAC: I need to know, and you've got to tell me.

ROSE: If you're going to ask what I think you're going to ask, please don't. I won't tell you.

MAC: If you don't I'll pull this shade off and stare at the sun as hard as I can.

ROSE: Don't be so... Alright, I'll tell you if I know. Just don't do anything reckless.

MAC: And you won't dodge the question, like everyone else does?

ROSE: No.

MAC: Then does the doctor think my eyes are worse than the last time he came?

ROSE: (*Quietly.*) I believe he does, yes.

MAC: I thought so. And am I going to be able to go back to school in September?

ROSE: No, Mac.

MAC: Ah.

Pause.

When *will* I be able to study again?

ROSE: Not for a good many months.

MAC: How many?

ROSE: Perhaps a year.

MAC: A whole year. My, that's hard.

ROSE: But you mustn't be depressed. Be patient now and get them thoroughly well or they'll trouble you again when it will be harder to spare them.

MAC: No. I will study and get through somehow. What do doctors know, anyway? It's all humbug. I'll do exactly what I want. Pass me that book.

ROSE: No, Mac. Listen to me. You know you've hurt your eyes reading by firelight and in the dusk and sitting up late, and now you'll have to pay for it. The doctor said so. You must be careful and do as he tells you or you might go – blind.

MAC: No.

ROSE: Yes, it's true.

MAC: Blind!

ROSE: He wanted us to tell you that nothing but complete rest would cure you. I know it's hard, but we'll all help you. I'll read all day long if you like, and lead you around, and wait on you and... Oh, don't cry, Mac.

MAC: (*In tears.*) I'm not crying.

He goes to wipe his eyes on his sleeve.

ROSE: No, don't rub them with that harsh woollen stuff. Let me bathe them for you. The doctor said they should be bathed regularly.

MAC: Alright. (*After a moment.*) You won't tell the others I cried, will you? I don't want them thinking I'm a baby.

ROSE: Oh Mac, anyone would be upset at the idea of being... No, of course I won't tell them.

MAC: Swear?

ROSE: I swear.

MAC: That's alright then.

ROSE: I'll go and fetch some cotton wool. Then I'll bathe your eyes.

MAC: (*Just before she goes.*) Rose...

ROSE: Yes, Mac?

MAC: Thank you for telling me.

JASON BODGER AND THE PRIORY GHOST

by Gene Kemp

JASON BODGER was the boss of Class 4Z and the terror of student teachers until the fatal day when 4Z went to visit the Priory. The rest of the class saw a few ancient relics, but JASON saw MATHILDE, a 14 year old girl who had been born eight centuries before. JASON and MATHILDE get to know each other across the centuries.

MATHILDE: But I'm not dead. It's you that's not right in the head.

JASON: (*Gloomily.*) You've been dead for centuries, you 'ave. About seven or eight. That's a long time.

MATHILDE: Don't be so stupid, fleabag that you are, boar fleabag. You can see I'm not dead. Look. I'm here. And it's now. And I'm real. Pinch my arm.

JASON does so.

Ouch! You didn't have to pinch that hard. You are one of the mad people, one of the funnies. If I were cruel like my sisters, I'd have you locked up. But I'm nice, I am. Don't pull that face. I'm very nice. And I shall be a great lady – stop laughing, won't you? Whereas you'll be a barmy prophet that people come for miles to see because you say crazy things and make them laugh with all that stuff about horseless chariots and carts and machines that fly in the air like birds.

JASON: You saw those yourself. You admitted it.

MATHILDE: It was a dream. When I was ill with the fever.

JASON: No, it was for real, I tell you. And there's other things, telly and cassettes and telecom and computers and nukes...

MATHILDE: What are nukes? Take that cross look off your face and tell me. Go on.

JASON: Nukes are very powerful weapons that can blow up the world, kill everything, all of us.

MATHILDE: Weapons like spears? Catapults? Bows and arrows?

JASON: No, not like them. Worse. Dangerous. To us all.

MATHILDE: Can I have one for the castle? To kill Antacill?

JASON: No, because it would kill everyone in your castle and forests, all the people and animals as well, so it wouldn't be any use, for we'd all be dead too.

MATHILDE: What a silly weapon. What use is that? Hundreds of years did you say? It took that long time to make rubbish like that? They must all be very stupid in your time. Like you.

Pause. JASON sulks.

If you are really an in-our-time person, you are barmy. And if not, you are the future because we are here now.

JASON: I'm the now person. I'm modern. You're gone, you are. Past it.

MATHILDE: I'm not past it. Do I look past it?

JASON: No, you look great. But you're still dead.

MATHILDE: I am not. You haven't happened yet.

JASON: I'm here, aren't I? So I must have happened.

MATHILDE: Why do you speak like us, if you're not one of us?

JASON: Telepathy.

MATHILDE: What?

JASON: Don't you know anything? Brain messages passed without any words. Our brains are translating what we're both saying. Like my jeans and tee-shirt have been changed into these scum-bag, flea-bitten clothes.

MATHILDE: You look better than you did in that stuff before.

JASON: When you were a ghost, you mean?

MATHILDE: I was not a ghost. I was ill and seeing things strangely.

JASON: When I met you, you were a ghost begging me to help you, just a bit of old history. You don't seem like a ghost now, but you are, because your time has really gone.

MATHILDE: You person of the future, you will stay and help me fight for the castle? You don't want to go back, do you?

JASON: I might.

MATHILDE: Why?

JASON: There's football and telly and junk food and a girl named Phrynne.

MATHILDE: Jason, you may be crazy like a hermit or a wise man, I don't know, but I'll race you to that tree. And I'll win.

JASON: You're on!

They run off.

By permission of Lawrence Pollinger Ltd. *Jason Bodger and the Priory Ghost* by Gene Kemp is published by Faber and Faber.

TO SERVE THEM ALL MY DAYS

by R.F. Delderfield
dramatised by Shaun McKenna

DAVY POWLETT-JONES was invalided out of the army in 1917, at the age of twenty, and has obtained a position as a teacher in a small school on Exmoor. DAVY is visiting his native Wales for a holiday shortly after the end of World War I. He is walking along the promenade at Rhos-on-Sea when a girl's hat flies down from the pier and lands at his feet.

A woman's hat falls from the flies. DAVY looks up.

BETH: (*Calling, off.*) I say! Hello! Hello there!

DAVY points questioningly at himself.

Could you possibly...? I'm so sorry.

DAVY: (*Picking up the hat, calling.*) I'll bring it up.

BETH: (*Off.*) No, no, I'll come down.

DAVY: But...

But she has gone. DAVY looks up, trying to catch sight of her.

BETH: (*Running on.*) What a silly thing to do. I was leaning right out over the pier railing, I didn't think about the wind.

DAVY: There was no need to come down. I was coming on the pier anyway. Now you've lost your tuppence.

BETH: Oh well. Tuppence won't break the bank. Thank you.

She takes the hat. An awkward pause.

DAVY: Well...

BETH: Well.

DAVY is trying hard to think of something to say.

Yes?

DAVY: It's a... (*Gestures vaguely, a bit desperately.*)

BETH: Yes, isn't it. I'm always lucky with the weather.

DAVY: Ah. Good. I mean...

Pause.

DAVY: (*Together.*) Are you with...?

BETH: (*Together.*) Perhaps we could...?

DAVY: After you.

BETH: No. You first.

DAVY: Well, I was wondering... Are you with anyone? Perhaps we could have some tea? Or coffee.

BETH: No.

DAVY: Oh, I er... Sorry.

BETH: I mean I'm not with anyone. I'm sorry. I've only just had some coffee on the pier. But we could walk along the front for a little way, couldn't we? Oh dear. First I throw my cap at you, now I'm inviting myself out. You'll think I do this sort of thing professionally.

DAVY: Not at all. I was going for a walk on the front anyway.

BETH: I thought you were going on the pier. (*Laughing at his dumbstruck look.*) I'm sorry. My sister's always telling me off for saying what I think, but I can't seem to help myself. What's your name?

DAVY: Powlett-Jones. David Powlett-Jones.

BETH: David! What luck. That's absolutely my favourite boy's name. It used to be Paul, until I had another look at the Acts of the Apostles. Paul was such a killjoy, wasn't he? But David was a proper old rake. (*Seeing his embarrassment.*) Oh Lord, I'm sorry. Elizabeth Marwood. I shall quite understand if you want to turn and flee.

DAVY: (*Putting out his hand.*) How do you do?

BETH: (*Shaking it.*) Hello. You're not fleeing then?

DAVY: Not yet.

BETH: I am glad. What a nice thing to happen on the first day of the holiday. My sister lives near here. I come up on my unpaid week each Spring. You were in the army, weren't you?

DAVY: (*Taken aback.*) How did you know?

BETH: Oh, all of you who were in the trenches have that same look, as though...

DAVY: Yes?

BETH: No. You don't want to talk about it. I'm always getting into trouble on the ward for poking my nose in.

DAVY: Are you a nurse?

BETH: Yes. In Swansea.

DAVY: You're not like any nurse I've ever met.

BETH: (*Laughing.*) Oh, I can be bossy if I have to, believe me.

DAVY: I wish I'd had a nurse like you.

BETH: Not a chance. Matron wouldn't let us probationers nurse the younger men. She seemed to think it might make them sit up and take notice too quickly.

DAVY: She was right. How old are you?

BETH: Nineteen. Nineteen today, as it happens.

DAVY: Really? Then we must celebrate. Let me buy you an ice. I mean, if you don't mind.

BETH: Of course I don't. If you're free we could have lunch. I know a cafe in town where the food isn't all that bad. Hell's teeth, listen to me. For all I know you've got a girl somewhere. You might even be married.

DAVY: I'd be lucky where I work.

BETH: Tell me all about it.

DAVY: Alright, if you like. Let's go along the prom as far
as Rhos. Then we'll have lunch, and after... well, I was
thinking of taking one of those afternoon charabanc trips
to Conway Castle. You're welcome to come along, but
I'll almost certainly bore you if you do.

BETH: I can't think of anything nicer.

DAVY: Oh. Oh good.

He holds out an arm, which she takes. They exit.

RULING PASSIONS

by Shaun McKenna

See note on RULING PASSIONS on page 38. The play is set in Paris in 1848. HENRIETTE DELUZY is an impressionable young governess to the children of the handsome young THEO, DUC DE PRASLIN. The DUC's wife is a neurotic, unstable woman. Here, the DUC visits HENRIETTE late one evening.

Evening. HENRIETTE sits reading at the table by the light of a lamp. THEO enters quietly, behind her.

THEO: You read too much.

HENRIETTE: (*Startled.*) I... (Realising.) Oh.

THEO: I did not mean to startle you.

HENRIETTE: (*Rising.*) The children are in bed, monsieur.

THEO: I should hope so. (*Of the book.*) You will damage your eyes.

Beat.

THEO: (*Together.*) I thought...

HENRIETTE: (*Together.*) Is there...?

Both laugh and stop. HENRIETTE gestures to THEO.

HENRIETTE: Have I done something wrong? Whatever it is, monsieur, it was unintentional, believe me.

THEO: You have done nothing wrong.

HENRIETTE: Then...?

THEO: My governess was tall and bony and cruel. I always vowed not to inflict such a creature on my children.

HENRIETTE: I have displeased you.

THEO: Quite the contrary. You have brought peace to my house.

HENRIETTE: (*Surprised, pleased.*) Oh.

THEO: To this wing, at any rate.

He looks to see how she will respond. She lowers her eyes.

This room of yours is a haven of warmth and calm. I envy that. You have made a great deal of difference to the children, you know.

HENRIETTE: They are lovely children.

THEO: I think so. But I am partial. Do you play cards?

HENRIETTE: I... A little. Raynald and I play Beggar My Neighbour.

THEO: Piquet?

HENRIETTE: No.

THEO: I must teach you something other than children's games. Beggar My Neighbour bores me, I'm afraid. And Happy Families seems always to have eluded me.

Beat.

I'm embarrassing you.

HENRIETTE: Not at all.

THEO: How did you come to be a governess?

Beat.

I'm intruding.

HENRIETTE: I don't mind. My father died when I was very small, my mother not long after. My grandfather sent me to a convent in Dieppe. I studied there, then taught.

THEO: And no doubt fell heartily in love with a slender curate.

HENRIETTE: Monsieur!

THEO: Have I hit the mark?

HENRIETTE: No, you are very wide. The directrice recommended me to Lady Hislop in Hertfordshire. French governesses were the rage.

THEO: Were you happy?

HENRIETTE: Very. I was not much above a girl, myself. But Nina and I did well together.

THEO: So you fell in love in England. (*Seeing her blush.*) Aha! A bull's eye.

HENRIETTE: (*Laughing.*) Perhaps the outer ring.

THEO: A curate?

HENRIETTE: A curate of remarkable ambition. He soon left me behind.

THEO: I'm sorry.

HENRIETTE: I did not mind too much.

THEO: So you have never been in love?

HENRIETTE: I don't believe love – that kind of love – is an experience I need to be a good governess. Or to be happy.

THEO: Oh, I'm not sure it's an experience that necessarily results in happiness. For anyone. A remarkably straightforward history. I envy you.

HENRIETTE: Me?

THEO: You haven't had to worry about continuing the family name. Or allying yourself to a great fortune.

HENRIETTE: I have never had that opportunity.

THEO: I married Frances for love. I was nineteen.

HENRIETTE does not reply.

The money was not unwelcome either, of course.
The estate in Corsica is superb.

HENRIETTE: I look forward to visiting it, with the children.

THEO: Paris is so tedious at this time of year. Shall we take a house in Dieppe for the summer?

HENRIETTE: I will go wherever you instruct.

THEO: June and July in Dieppe. You can revisit your old haunts.

HENRIETTE: I have no 'old haunts'.

THEO: Then Melun for the autumn. The orchards are glorious in September. Leaves the colour of your hair.

He looks at her. Beat.

I cannot believe you have never been in love.

HENRIETTE: Believe it.

THEO: You have so much to look forward to.

HENRIETTE: It may never happen.

THEO: Oh, it will. It will.

HOW GREEN WAS MY VALLEY

by Richard Llewellyn
dramatised by Shaun McKenna

See note on the play on page 17. The play is set in South Wales in the last years of Queen Victoria's reign. HUW MORGAN is 17 and here has arranged to meet CEINWEN PHILLIPS, also 17, on the mountain, 'to listen to the nightingales.' HUW is embarrassed by CEINWEN's obvious attraction to him.

CEINWEN stands with a red wicker basket over her arm.

CEINWEN: Hullo, Huw.

HUW: What was that stuff on your letter?

CEINWEN: Perfume. Did you like it?

HUW: I thought I would be sick.

CEINWEN: (*Hurt.*) Oh.

HUW: (*Seeing he has hurt her.*) Joking I am, girl. I came, didn't I? Your hair is up.

CEINWEN: This long time. I... I am very glad to see you.

HUW: A surprise, eh?

CEINWEN: I have come to hear the nightingales. Yes, you have promised. I found out your shift, see. My father is gone to Dowlais so I can stay late. (*Showing him the basket.*) Look.

HUW: What is that?

CEINWEN: To eat. Are we going to be up here all night with nothing in our bellies but old sounds and screeches?

HUW: All night? I have got choir practice at seven o'clock.

CEINWEN: Let seven o'clock come. Sit with me.

They sit.

Do you know why I really asked you to meet me?

HUW: To hear the nightingales?

CEINWEN: I want you to take me to the Town Hall for the acting.

HUW: What acting?

CEINWEN: The actors are coming for two nights. I will never be allowed to mention it at home, never mind go.

HUW: Why do you want to?

CEINWEN: I want to be an actress. I am sick to the heart of the coal yard. Actress, me.

HUW: No place at home for you, if you go.

CEINWEN: So? Not a tear from me if I never see them again.

HUW: A hard life, though, and wicked people.

CEINWEN: If Mr Irving is wicked, I will be wicked too.

HUW: Who's Mr Irving?

CEINWEN: Good God, man, they are going mad for him in London. Will you take me to the acting? Tuesday week?

HUW: I expect so.

She hands him a piece of pie.

CEINWEN: Here.

HUW: (*Eating.*) Did you cook this?

CEINWEN: Who else? Is it poison?

HUW: No. No, you are a cook.

CEINWEN: A bit heavy in the pastry and not enough sage with the meat.

HUW: I will have more.

CEINWEN: A flattery.

HUW: If it was bad I would leave it.

CEINWEN: Spoilt at home, you. A job your wife will have.

HUW: Only as good as I get now, I want.

CEINWEN: You would drive the girl mad, and she would throw a couple of dishes at you, and you would smash every pot on the dresser with temper. If you did it to me, I would wait for you to sleep and kill you with one hit.

HUW: No hope of that, anyway.

CEINWEN: (*Changing tack.*) It is good to marry and have a little house of your own. Fresh with paint, and your own furniture where you want it. With a little bit of garden. A couple of hens to scratch. And babies. Will you marry me, Huw?

HUW: We are too young.

CEINWEN: My Mama married from school. We are both working.

HUW: I want to be earning more, first.

CEINWEN: Say yes, Huw.

HUW: I cannot. Not now.

CEINWEN: Do you like me?

HUW: Yes.

CEINWEN: Do you remember when we kissed?

HUW: Yes.

CEINWEN: Did you like it?

HUW: Yes.

CEINWEN: Me, too.

Pause.

HUW: Shall I kiss you now?

CEINWEN: If you want.

HUW leans over to kiss her.

Oh Huw.

HOW GREEN WAS MY VALLEY

by Richard Llewellyn
dramatised by Shaun McKenna

See note on the play on page 17. The play is set in South Wales in the last years of Queen Victoria's reign. HUW MORGAN is 17 and he has abandoned a promising academic career to work in the coal mines with the rest of his family. His elder sister, ANGHARAD, is 20 and is married to IESTYN EVANS, a local colliery owner. IESTYN is away fighting the Boer War and ANGHARAD has returned to the Evans' house in the valley. She has always been in love with the local preacher, MR GRUFFYDD, who returned her love but was too poor to consider marrying her. ANGHARAD and HUW meet in the garden of the Evans' house.

ANGHARAD: I look ill and I should take care of myself. Everyone says so.

HUW: It is inside you. Mama said it was.

Pause.

ANGHARAD: You have grown.

HUW: Remember when you used to give me sweets to go to Sunday school?

ANGHARAD: And had them back from you in class? Shame, eh?

HUW: No shame. You liked a couple of sweets.

ANGHARAD: (*Tears in her eyes.*) A fool I am. Sit, Huw, and have to eat. Now then, a bit of sense for a change. You are coming from that old pit.

HUW: (*Laughing.*) Indeed I am not. So there.

ANGHARAD: There is lovely to hear a laugh.

HUW: Come over to the house, girl. You shall hear plenty and have a few, too.

ANGHARAD: I... I cannot. (*Pulling herself together.*) Have some cake.

HUW: Did Mrs Nicholas make it?

ANGHARAD: She did. But I don't think it is poisoned.

HUW: A bitch, that one.

ANGHARAD: Pedigree. I am sour to be near her.

HUW: Send her away.

ANGHARAD: I cannot. She has been with the family forty-seven years – and sixty times a day she tells me so. Besides, the house is beautiful, and not a turn of the hand from me. But I could scream whenever she comes near me.

HUW: A bitch.

ANGHARAD: A bitch.

They laugh, ANGHARAD a little more than is warranted.

Come on, let's have a chase around the garden. Catch me.

She runs from him. HUW, laughing, gives chase and soon they are dodging round the table and chairs, laughing. HUW catches her and they fall into a heap.

Oh, there is good, Huw.

HUW: Yes, indeed.

ANGHARAD: How is everybody we used to know?

HUW: Good. Eunice and Eiluned Jenkins are married. Eunice is at home, and Eiluned has gone to London to keep a dairy. Maldwyn Hughes has gone to be a doctor. Rhys Howell is in a solicitor's office in town and sends home ten shillings a week. And... And Mr Gruffydd is still first up and last to bed. And he can still be heard from one end of the valley to the other and no strain.

ANGHARAD: How is he?

HUW: Not as he was.

ANGHARAD: Is he ill?

HUW: Inside. In his eyes and voice. Like you.

ANGHARAD: Oh Huw. You were the only one. No-one else cared. You told him. (*She starts to cry.*)

HUW: Come on, girl. Nothing to cry for, is there?

He holds her until she is still.

ANGHARAD: First cry. Never before. That is why.

HUW: All over now.

ANGHARAD: All over. Thank God.

HUW: Angharad...

ANGHARAD: Yes?

HUW: Mr Gruffydd will be coming here. This afternoon.

ANGHARAD: Oh. I am... I am glad. There is no going back, Huw.

HUW: No.

ANGHARAD: No going back.

JANE EYRE

by Charlotte Bronte
dramatised by Shaun McKenna

The story needs little introduction. JANE EYRE has fled
Thornfield on the day of her marriage, after discovering that
her husband-to-be had a wife still living. She wandered on the
Yorkshire moors for some time and was taken in by the family
of ST JOHN RIVERS, a clergyman. Having recovered her
health, she takes an assumed name and starts to teach at the
church school and RIVERS falls in love with her.

JANE: You told me you have an important matter to
broach, Mr Rivers? Is it the school?

Pause.

Has there been some fault on my part? Some lack of
discretion.

RIVERS: You have been discreet enough.

JANE: Then please, whatever it is, tell me.

RIVERS: You tell me.

JANE: You are speaking in riddles. I don't understand.
You have never behaved like this before.

RIVERS: These are unusual circumstances, Jane Eyre.

JANE: Not so unusual that... What did you call me?

RIVERS: I called you by your name.

Pause.

Do you deny it?

JANE: No.

RIVERS: Twenty years ago, a poor curate fell in love with
a rich man's daughter. The rich man opposed the match

but she married her curate all the same and was disowned. Within two years they were both dead, laid quietly side by side under one slab. They left a daughter, which charity received into its lap – a cold, hard, Reed-like charity. You start. Do you hear a noise? Mrs Reed kept the infant ten years then sent it to Lowood School, where the child later became a teacher. Perhaps you knew her? Her story is very similar to yours. She left Lowood to become a governess, her charge the ward of a Mr Rochester of Thornfield Hall.

JANE: Mr Rivers!

RIVERS: I can guess your feelings but restrain them awhile. I must tell this story to the end. What befell her at Thornfield I do not know but she left, suddenly. At around the time you collapsed on our doorstep.

JANE: How do you know this?

RIVERS: Through Mr Briggs, our family solicitor.

JANE: Have you any news of Mr Rochester?

RIVERS: Hush. Don't concern yourself with trifles. There is more.

JANE: Perhaps Mr Briggs will have more news of Mr Rochester than you.

RIVERS: Perhaps. Mr Briggs has been trying to locate you.

JANE: For what purpose?

RIVERS: Merely to inform you that you are a rich woman, nothing more.

JANE: I? A rich woman?

RIVERS: You are quite an heiress.

Pause.

JANE: How much am I worth?

RIVERS: Nothing to speak of. Twenty thousand pounds, less thirty guineas bequeathed to your cousins for mourning rings.

JANE: What are you telling me, Mr Rivers? For heaven's sake, speak! Quickly! I dare not hope... Is it true? Are you my cousin?

RIVERS: I, and Diana, and Mary.

Pause

Why are you weeping?

JANE: Because... I have never had anything that I can truly call my own. And now not only do I have a family – they prove to be my dearest friends and companions.

RIVERS: And that you are worth a fortune.

JANE: What is money compared to that? But how can it be? I knew I had an uncle, Mrs Reed told me just before she died, but...

RIVERS: Your mother was my father's sister. My late uncle in Madeira was your uncle too. He showed remorse, it seems, at the last.

JANE: May God reward him for it. You are sure, St John? I may call you St John now?

RIVERS: If you are Jane Eyre, I am sure. And you may call me St John.

JANE: I am Jane Eyre.

RIVERS: And you are rich.

JANE: We are rich. Do you think I could take twenty thousand pounds and not share it with you? What would I do with such a sum? I can scarcely imagine it or what it would make of my life. But you, I, Diana, Mary – five thousand for each of us would ensure our modest comfort and freedom for life. What would you do with five thousand pounds, St John?

RIVERS: I... I would use it for my work.

JANE: And give more joy to the world than I could ever do with velvet gowns and satin slippers. There, it is decided. Five thousand pounds apiece.

RIVERS: You must think it over. It is too much, far too generous. You cannot...

JANE: If you think to change my mind, St John, you do not know me very well. You came to my rescue when I was close to death. This division of mere money is scant repayment.

RIVERS: Do not disdain money, Jane. In this world, without it...

JANE: I do not disdain it. But I have seen wealthy women, seen them too closely. Money may bring advantages but in the scale of life it does not weigh so heavily. Come, let us tell Diana and Mary.

THE POSTMAN ALWAYS RINGS TWICE

by James M. Cain
dramatised by Shaun McKenna

See note on the dramatisation on page 25. CORA
PAPADAKIS, the beautiful young wife of a Greek lunch-room
owner in Southern California, has been having an affair with the
hired help, FRANK CHAMBERS. They have worked out a
plan to kill her husband. Now they are about to put the plan into
operation.

CORA: Well?

FRANK: He don't suspect a thing.

CORA: Why would he?

FRANK: You know what to do?

CORA: We've been over it a hundred times.

FRANK: So tell me.

CORA: You don't trust me, do you?

FRANK: I've never done anything like this before.

CORA: You think I have?

FRANK: Scared?

CORA: No. (*Fierce.*) NO!

FRANK: Here. I got the ball bearings. You got the sugar bag?

CORA: (*Handing it to him.*) There.

*FRANK drops the ball bearings into the sugar bag. CORA
stares at the bag.*

FRANK: Wad 'em down tight.

She does so.

Tie a knot.

It is starting to resemble a weapon.

CORA: Like that?

FRANK: Yeah. That'll make a pretty good blackjack. Now, you put the water in my room like I'm ready to shave. That's what I'll say I did. Then I remembered I left the car out front so I went out to move it.

CORA: Soon as I hear him get in the tub I go in the bathroom for a towel and clip him from behind. Then I hold him under till he drowns.

FRANK: I'll give a blast on the horn if anyone comes. OK, what next?

CORA: I...

FRANK: Cora!

CORA: I know, I do know. Don't rush me. I leave the water running and climb out of the window and on to the porch roof. Then I climb down the stepladder. You put the stepladder there?

FRANK: Half an hour ago.

CORA: Then I give you the blackjack and come back in the kitchen.

FRANK: I move the stepladder. Then I put the ball bearings back in the garage, throw away the sugar bag, put the car in, go up to my room and start to shave. When the water starts to drip through into the kitchen...

CORA: I call you. You break down the door, we find him. I call an ambulance. But it's too late.

FRANK: Right.

CORA: Right.

Pause.

You and me, Frank?

FRANK: You and me. On top of our mountain where nobody can touch us. Just you and me and God's clean air and all the space in the world.

CORA: You do love me, don't you, Frank.

FRANK: Who couldn't love a hellcat like you.

Pause.

CORA: You'd better get out front. Get in the car.

FRANK: We're playing it like we're going to tell it, right?

CORA: Right. You hear or see anything, hit that horn.

FRANK: OK.

FRANK exits. CORA looks down at the weapon in her hand.

CORA: (*Under her breath.*) I'm a hellcat. I'm a hellcat.

She exits upstairs.

MEETING JACK

by Shaun McKenna

See note on the play on page 46. It is 1908, on the Polynesian island of Malaita, where cannibalism is still rife. CHARMIAN LONDON, the mid-20s wife of the American writer JACK LONDON, and MARTIN PRIDDY, a naive young Englishman, have taken refuge in the hut of CAULDFIELD, the local missionary. They have been attacked by a native bent on murder, and have overpowered him – but not before he killed the missionary's servant, MOSES. Now the native is tied up in the middle of the floor.

CHARMIAN: Tighter.

PRIDDY: We'll cut off his circulation.

CHARMIAN: Do you think I care? Tie him tighter.

PRIDDY: He's badly wounded. He might die.

CHARMIAN: I don't believe I'm hearing this.

PRIDDY: Charmian...

CHARMIAN: Put the sonofabitch out of his misery.

PRIDDY: Of course not.

CHARMIAN: He tried to kill us.

PRIDDY: That's no reason to...

CHARMIAN: Shoot him!

PRIDDY: I couldn't possibly.

CHARMIAN: Stop being so goddamn English.

PRIDDY: He's out of action. He's wounded. (*Shouting.*) *I'm not going to kill him in cold blood.*

CHARMIAN: He's a goddamn cannibal. And the rest of them will show up soon.

PRIDDY: If there were others, they'd have been here by now.

CHARMIAN: Give me the gun.

PRIDDY: No.

CHARMIAN: Give it to me.

PRIDDY: NO!

CHARMIAN: You're pathetic.

PRIDDY: Very probably.

CHARMIAN: He's going to bleed to death in any case.

PRIDDY: We'll bandage him as best we can.

CHARMIAN: Forget it.

PRIDDY: I'm in charge here.

CHARMIAN: Says who?

PRIDDY: We'll bind up his wound. And we'll talk to him, keep him awake.

CHARMIAN: In God's name, why?

PRIDDY: It's the only thing to do.

CHARMIAN: Kill him.

PRIDDY: This is a mission. A house of God. We can't kill him here.

He investigates the wounded man.

He's out cold.

CHARMIAN: (*After a moment.*) I think I panicked.

PRIDDY: Yes. Poor Moses.

CHARMIAN: It must have been quick. I don't suppose he knew much about it.

PRIDDY: A knife to the throat.

CHARMIAN: Don't.

PRIDDY: My worst nightmare.

CHARMIAN: He was doing his duty. Protecting us.

PRIDDY: He was doing it for Caulfield. And God.

CHARMIAN: I didn't know you were so religious.

PRIDDY: Neither did I.

Pause.

CHARMIAN: Is he still breathing?

PRIDDY: Yes. Sun'll be up soon.

CHARMIAN: Jack will come and find us.

PRIDDY: What will you tell him?

CHARMIAN: You promised to protect me.

PRIDDY: Yes.

CHARMIAN: I haven't come to any harm.

PRIDDY: No. So there's no need to mention any of this. Is there?

Beat.

CHARMIAN: Thank you, Martin.

PRIDDY: My pleasure.

CHARMIAN: (*Struck by the absurdity of it.*) Was it?

PRIDDY: What?

CHARMIAN: Your pleasure?

PRIDDY laughs shortly. CHARMIAN chuckles. Soon they are both laughing uproariously.

MADDIE

by Shaun McKenna,
Steven Dexter and Stephen Keeling

This musical comedy premiered at Salisbury in 1996 and opened in the West End in the autumn of 1997. It concerns the ghost of MADDIE, a 1920s flapper, who possesses the body of Jan, wife of NICK CHEYNEY. Here, in JAN CHEYNEY's body, MADDIE has just behaved outrageously at a sedate high society party. NICK has dragged her away, but she is intent on having fun and has brought a bottle of champagne with her. The scene is San Francisco, 1981. The libretto is published by Warner-Chappell.

MADDIE: Put me down.

> *NICK deposits her unceremoniously and, immediately, she plants a kiss on his mouth. He pushes her away.*

NICK: Stop this!

MADDIE: Don't tell me this ain't better than you get from June, Joan...

NICK: Jan.

MADDIE: Right.

NICK: What have you done to her?

MADDIE: Don't worry. She's quite safe.

NICK: Where is she?

MADDIE: (*Gesturing vaguely.*) Out there, someplace. Probably having the time of her life.

NICK: Does she know you're here?

MADDIE: I'm not sure. I don't think so. She'd pop right back in if I gave her half a chance but I'm having too much fun. I'm holding on hard, sheik. Kiss me.

NICK: No.

MADDIE: Go on. Pretend I'm Jane, Jean...

NICK: Jan! I want her back.

MADDIE: Later.

NICK: Now!

MADDIE: You need a little drinkie.

NICK: I do not need a little drinkie.

MADDIE: Just a mouthful. And I'll let her back in.

NICK: You promise?

MADDIE: Finger wet, finger dry.

NICK: OK, OK. One mouthful.

He takes the bottle and takes a small slug. MADDIE puts her hand to her head.

MADDIE: Nicky. I don't feel so good.

NICK: Jan!

He runs and embraces her. She kisses him fervently.

MADDIE: Hey, mister, you're a good kisser.

NICK lets out a roar of anger.

NICK: You promised.

MADDIE: I lied.

She runs away. With a roar, NICK chases after her, but she is too fast for him. He comes to a stop, breathless.

No stamina! Hey, don't drink it all.

NICK: It's great champagne.

MADDIE: The real McCoy. Right off the boat! Where do you get hooch like this?

NICK: The liquor store.

MADDIE: The bootlegger has a store?

NICK: No. Prohibition's over, Maddie. Since long before I was born.

MADDIE: (*Looking out front, surprised.*) What's that?

NICK: The Golden Gate Bridge.

MADDIE: What happened to the ferries?

NICK: They got rid of them.

MADDIE: That's stupid. They were fun.

NICK: (*Handing her the champagne.*) Here.

MADDIE: I can't believe how much things have changed.

NICK: It's been a long time, Maddie.

MADDIE: What year is it anyway?

NICK: 1981.

MADDIE: Boy! That's... er... fifty-seven years I've missed out on.

NICK: Fifty-five.

MADDIE: What's the diff. I always hated math. Say, that means I'm...

NICK: Seventy-six.

MADDIE: Seventy-six!

She looks sad for a moment, then breaks out of it.

Oh, who cares! The main thing is, I'm back.

NICK: And how.

MADDIE: It's so wonderful just to stretch again! To breathe again. And to kiss...

She kisses him. NICK responds, for a moment, then pushes her away gently.

NICK: Bad idea.

MADDIE: One little kiss won't hurt you.

NICK: (*Struggling with himself.*) No.

MADDIE: Why not?

NICK: Because I don't want to be unfaithful to my wife. (*He stops himself.*) But you are my wife! Sort of. Jesus, I must be the first man since Moses to discover a new kind of sin.

MADDIE: (*Gently.*) Kiss me, Nicky.

NICK: You're making things real difficult, you know that?

THE TENANT OF WILDFELL HALL

by Anne Bronte

HELEN is unhappily married to ARTHUR HUNTINGDON, who drinks and physically abuses her. He also flirts – or worse – with other women, whom he invites to their house. The novel is set in the 1840s.

ARTHUR: Are you very angry?

HELEN: This is no jest, Arthur, unless you think it a jest to lose my affection forever.

ARTHUR: (*Laughing.*) What? So bitter?

He grabs her hand. She pulls it away. He laughs.

Then I must go down on my knees. (*Kneeling, mockingly.*) Forgive me, Helen! Dear Helen – forgive me, and I'll never do it again.

He takes a handkerchief from his pocket and pretends to sob.

HELEN: (*Turning to go.*) I cannot talk to you.

ARTHUR: (*Grabbing her.*) No, by heaven. You shan't escape me so. Do not put yourself in such a passion. Your face has turned completely white. I swear, my dear, you will kill yourself if you carry on like this.

HELEN: Let me go, then.

ARTHUR: This is all nonsense, Helen. A jest, a mere nothing, not worth a thought. Will you never learn that you have nothing to fear from me? That I love you wholly and entirely? Or – if I do ever give a thought to another, you need not consider it, for those fancies are here and gone like a flash of lightning while my love for you burns steadily and forever like the sun.

HELEN: Listen to me...

ARTHUR: Oh, you little tyrant, aren't you reassured yet? Are you determined to have another jealous fury?

HELEN: I am perfectly calm. Feel my hand. Quite steady.

ARTHUR: So?

HELEN: You may think it very fine to amuse yourself with rousing my jealousy. But take care you don't rouse my hate instead. If you ever manage to extinguish my love, it will be no easy matter for you to kindle it again.

ARTHUR: I'm sorry, Helen. I won't repeat the offence. It meant nothing. I had taken too much wine, that is all.

HELEN: You often take too much wine – and I detest it. Don't look so shocked. I have never mentioned it before because I was too ashamed to acknowledge that my husband was a drunkard. But it distresses me and it disgusts me, Arthur. If you don't take pains to stop it, the habit will grow upon you. But your attentions to Lady Lowborough tonight had nothing to do with wine. You knew exactly what you were doing.

ARTHUR: (*Sulky.*) I have already apologised. I am sorry.

HELEN: Sorry that I saw you, no doubt.

ARTHUR: If you had not seen me, it would have done no harm.

HELEN: You think not?

ARTHUR: No. After all, what have I done? It's nothing – unless you choose to make it something.

HELEN: What would her husband have said, had he seen? Or what would you have done had Lord Lowborough acted to me as you have to his wife?

ARTHUR: I would have blown his brains out.

HELEN: So how can you call it nothing? You have trifled with your friend's feelings and with mine. You have tried to steal a woman's affections from her husband, something he values more than gold. Are marriage vows a jest? Is it nothing to make it your sport to break them and to tempt another to do the same? Can I love a man that does such things and coolly maintains that it is nothing?

ARTHUR: You are breaking your marriage vows yourself. You promised to honour and obey me and now you are threatening me and hectoring me and accusing me, and calling me worse than a highwayman. Were you not bearing our child, Helen, I would not submit to it so calmly. I won't be dictated to by anyone, Helen, particularly not a woman and particularly not my wife.

HELEN: What will you do then? Go on with it till I hate you? Then accuse me of breaking my vows?

Pause.

ARTHUR: You will never hate me. You cannot hate me, as long as I love you.

HELEN: You are very confident in that assertion.

ARTHUR: Come now, Helen, won't you forgive me?

HELEN: If I do, you will repeat the offence.

ARTHUR: I swear I will not.

HELEN: I wish I could have confidence in your oath.

ARTHUR: Try me and see.

Pause.

HELEN: Very well. I accept your word.

ARTHUR: And forgive me?

She nods. He brightens immediately.

Come then. Our guests will be wondering where we are.

EIGHT COUSINS
or THE AUNT HILL

by Louisa May Alcott

ROSE is 14, recently orphaned, and now living with her father's family in the Southern States of America. The time is the 1860s. ROSE has been unable to settle – until she meets the family's 15 year old servant-girl PHEBE. The scene is the kitchen, where PHEBE is working.

ROSE pokes her head around the kitchen door.

PHEBE: Morning, miss.

ROSE: Did I hear a mocking bird?

PHEBE: A mocking bird? Did you?

ROSE: I could have sworn I did.

PHEBE: I should call it a Phebe-bird.

ROSE: Where did it go?

PHEBE: It's still here.

ROSE: Where?

PHEBE: Here. In my throat. Do you want to hear it?

ROSE: Yes, please.

ROSE comes fully into the room. PHEBE whistles the call of the mocking bird.

That's wonderful. Who taught you?

PHEBE: The birds.

ROSE: That's very clever. I can sing, but nothing as fine as that. What's your name?

PHEBE: Phebe Moore.

ROSE: I've heard of Phebe-birds, but I don't believe the real ones could mop the floor as you're doing. Can I stay and watch. It's lonely in the parlour.

PHEBE: If you want to.

ROSE: It must be fun to swash the water about and dig out the soap. Can I try?

PHEBE: Your aunt might not like it.

ROSE: I suppose not.

PHEBE: And you'd soon get tired – you look rather peaky. You'd better just watch, then you can stay tidy.

ROSE: Do you help your mother a good deal?

PHEBE: I don't have any folks.

ROSE: (*Sadly.*) Neither do I, now. Where do you live?

PHEBE: Here, I hope. They need someone to help. I've come for a week's trial.

ROSE: I hope you'll stay. It is very dull here.

PHEBE: I hope so, too. I'm fifteen now and old enough to earn my own living. You've come to stay for a while, haven't you?

ROSE: Yes, till my uncle comes. He's my guardian now and I don't know what he plans to do with me. Do you have a guardian?

PHEBE: Sakes, no! I was left on the poor-house steps when I was a little mite of a baby, and Miss Rogers took a liking to me so I've been there ever since. But she's dead now and I take care of myself.

ROSE: That's very interesting – like something out of a book. Do you like books?

PHEBE: Yes, but I don't have any. When I have spare time I run off into the woods. That rests me more than stories. I suppose you've had lots of schooling.

ROSE: Yes, I've been at boarding school for more than a year and I'm almost dead with lessons. The more I got, the more Miss Power gave me and I was so miserable I almost cried my eyes out. Papa never gave me hard things to do – I liked it when he taught me. But he's... well, he's gone now. (*She starts to feel sad again.*)

PHEBE: You're not alone, though, not with all those folks belonging to you and all so rich and clever. You'll be petted to pieces, the housekeeper says, because you're the only girl in the family.

ROSE: But that's one of the problems. I've got six aunts and they all want me and I don't know any of them very well. Papa names this place the Aunt-Hill, and now I see why. And all those cousins, all boys, so loud and boisterous and... I'm not sure I shall like it here at all.

PHEBE: You'll get used to it.

ROSE: I suppose so. Of course, it would be easier if I had a friend.

PHEBE: You'll make friends with your cousins.

ROSE: But they're all boys! I want a... Say, Phebe, you wouldn't like to be my friend, would you?

PHEBE: (*After a moment.*) You know something, Miss Rose? That's be fine by me.

ROSE: Oh, I'm glad. Let's shake hands on it.

JANE EYRE

by Charlotte Bronte
dramatised by Shaun McKenna

See note on the play on page 18. In this scene, JANE EYRE, a governess at Thornfield Hall, is summoned to the bedside of her dying aunt, MRS REED, who brought her up brutally.

MRS REED: Are you Jane Eyre?

JANE: I am Jane Eyre.

MRS REED: Sit up! Don't annoy me with holding the bedclothes fast. Jane Eyre! I have had more trouble with that child than anyone would believe. Such a burden to be left on my hands – and so much annoyance as she caused me, daily and hourly, with her incomprehensible disposition and her sudden starts of temper and her continual, unnatural watching of one's movements. They had the fever at Lowood School, you know. Many of the girls died. She did not die.

JANE: I am here, aunt.

MRS REED: I wish she had died.

JANE: Why did you hate her so?

MRS REED: I always disliked her mother. She was my husband's only sister and always his favourite. He loved her more than he loved me, and I was his wife. He doted on that sickly, squalling baby, too. He cared more for her than for his own children, my children.

JANE: And that was the reason?

MRS REED: Who are you? Go away. Have you seen John? Tell him not to torment me with letters begging money. I have no more money to give him, he has quite ruined me. I must shut up half the house and

send off half the servants. You look familiar. Are you
sure you are a nurse? You look like... someone...

JANE: Hush, Aunt.

MRS REED: Why do you call me aunt?

JANE: You are my aunt. I said once that I would never call
you Aunt again. I said I would never forgive you. But
I do. I forgive you, Aunt Reed.

MRS REED: What for? What have you to forgive me for?
Who are you? I do not want your forgiveness. Just tell
John to stop threatening me. He threatens to kill himself,
you know, if I do not send him twenty guineas. I do not
have twenty guineas.

JANE: Rest, now. Try to sleep.

MRS REED: You are Jane Eyre.

JANE: We can speak later. Rest, now. Calm yourself.

MRS REED: I'm afraid I am not well. I wanted to see Jane
Eyre and now I think I do see her.

JANE: Bessie sent her husband to Thornfield to fetch me.
I came straight away.

MRS REED: I need to find Jane Eyre.

JANE: Why? What do you want to say to her?

MRS REED: I have wronged her.

JANE: (*Moved.*) You would say that to her?

MRS REED: Twice. I have wronged her twice. Once by
breaking my promise to my husband to bring her up as
my own child. And the second... She spoke so violently
to me that I was pleased to get rid of her. And then I had
a letter. Here. Under my pillow. Give it to Jane Eyre.

*She takes the letter and hands it to JANE, who opens it and
reads it.*

From John Eyre in Madeira. Her uncle. He wanted to adopt her. He was rich and childless. I told him she was dead. She was such a passionate, vindictive girl. She said things to me that she should never have thought.

JANE: That was a long time ago, aunt. I was only a child.

MRS REED: I never forgave her.

JANE: She has forgiven you.

MRS REED: No, now she will write to her uncle and blacken my name. Well, what of it? I shall be dead by then. She may do her worst.

JANE: Let us be reconciled, Aunt.

She leans over the bed and tries to kiss MRS REED.

MRS REED: What are you doing? Leave me alone. You're paid to nurse me, not to touch me. Who are you? You are not my nurse. Have you come to smother me? Help! Help!

JANE: Love me or hate me, then, as you will. You have my full and free forgiveness. Ask now for God's and be at peace.

MRS REED: Peace? What is peace?

JANE exits.

NORTHANGER ABBEY

by Jane Austen

Impressionable and romantic young CATHERINE MORLAND has been staying with her friend ELEANOR TILNEY at the family home of Northanger Abbey. HENRY TILNEY has fallen in love with CATHERINE and his father has heard of it. ELEANOR now has to break some terrible news to CATHERINE.

ELEANOR: Oh, Catherine, I cannot bear it! I come to you on such an errand.

CATHERINE: Errand? To me?

ELEANOR: How shall I tell you? Oh, how shall I tell you?

CATHERINE: Is it a messenger from Woodston?

ELEANOR: No, it is nobody from Woodston. It is my father himself.

CATHERINE: Your father?

ELEANOR: You are too good, I know, to think the worse of me for bringing the news I am obliged to. And I am unwilling to. After what has lately passed between us, so happily, so thankfully – I had hoped you would be able to stay on here for many weeks to come...

CATHERINE: Are we to part?

ELEANOR: Yes, my dear. My father has remembered an engagement that takes our whole family away on Monday to Lord Longtown's, near Hereford. Explanation and apology are equally impossible. I cannot attempt either.

CATHERINE: Eleanor, my dear, do not be so distressed. I can finish my visit here at any time – or you could come to me. Come to me at Fullerton when you return from this Lord's.

ELEANOR: It will not be in my power.

CATHERINE: Then come when you can.

ELEANOR is too embarrassed to answer.

This is not so dreadful. You are all leaving on Monday, you say. Then there is time for me to say my goodbyes properly to your family. I need not leave until just before you do. I can go on Monday very well. I dare say your father will send a servant with me half the way – to Salisbury, say. Then I am only nine miles from home.

ELEANOR: Oh Catherine, if only it were settled so. That is but the least you could expect. But how can I tell you? Tomorrow morning is fixed for your leaving us, and not even the hour is left to your choice; the carriage is ordered and will be here at seven o'clock, and no servant will be offered you.

CATHERINE is so shocked she has to sit down.

I could hardly believe my senses when I heard it; and no displeasure, no resentment that you can feel at this moment – however great, however just – is more than I myself. Oh, that I could make this better. What will your father and mother say? After courting you from the protection of real friends to this, twice the distance from your home, to drive you out of the house without even decent civility...

CATHERINE: What have I done?

ELEANOR: Please do not lay the blame for this on me. I am horrified, mortified, but what can I do? He is my father.

CATHERINE: Have I offended him?

ELEANOR: I do not see how you could have done so. His temper is not happy and something has happened just now to unruffle it to an uncommon degree – some disappointment, some vexation which just now seems important – but I cannot see how you might be connected with it.

CATHERINE: (*Upset, speaking carefully.*) If I have offended him, I am very sorry. It was the last thing I would willingly have done. But do not be unhappy, Eleanor. An engagement must be kept. I am only sorry it was not recollected sooner, that I might have written home. But it is of no consequence.

ELEANOR: I hope, for your safety, that it is of no consequence to you. It is of great consequence to everyone else – to comfort, appearance, propriety, to your family, to the world. Were your friends, the Allens, still in Bath you might go to them with comparative ease; a few hours would take you there; but a journey of seventy miles, to be taken post by you, at your age, alone, unattended.

CATHERINE: Oh, the journey is nothing. Do not think of that. And if we are to part, a few hours sooner or later makes no difference. I can be ready by seven. Let me be called in time.

ELEANOR: Oh Catherine...

CATHERINE: I shall see you in the morning, dear friend.

ELEANOR: Will you sleep?

CATHERINE: I always sleep.

ELEANOR: And you are not too distressed?

CATHERINE: Of course not.

ELEANOR: Then goodnight, my dear, dear friend.

CATHERINE: Goodnight, Eleanor.

ELEANOR leaves. CATHERINE bursts into tears.

GOOD WIVES

by Louisa May Alcott

JO and AMY are sisters, in 1870s America. JO is a budding writer and spends much of her time working in her room. This causes the more sociable and fashionable AMY some concern and she decides to do something about it.

AMY: Come, Jo, it's time.

JO: For what?

AMY: You don't mean to say you have forgotten? You promised to make half a dozen calls with me today.

JO: I've done a great many rash and foolish things in my time, Amy, but I don't think I was ever mad enough to say I'd make six calls in one day, when a single one upsets me for a week.

AMY: Yes you did. It was a bargain between us. I was to finish that drawing of Beth for you, and you were to go properly with me and return our neighbours' visits.

JO: If it was fair. That was in the bond, Shylock. I stand to the letter of the bond. There's a pile of clouds in the east. It's not fair and I don't go.

AMY: That's shirking. It's a lovely day, no prospect of rain. And you pride yourself on keeping promises, so be honourable. Come and do your duty and then be at peace for another six months.

JO: (*Putting down her pen and closing her books with a deep sigh.*) Very well, Amy.

AMY: Jo March, you are perverse enough to provoke a saint! You surely don't intend to go calling in that state!

JO: Why not?

AMY: Go and change.

JO: I'm cool and comfortable, and perfectly neat. I'm dressed quite properly for a dusty walk on a warm day. If people care more for my clothes than they do for me, I don't wish to see them.

AMY: Jo!

JO: You can dress for us both and be as elegant as you please. It pays for you to be fine, but it doesn't for me. Furbelows only worry me.

AMY: Oh dear, now you're in a contrary state and will drive me distracted before I get you properly ready. Jo, come and help me do the proper thing, the polite thing. You can talk so well, look so aristocratic in your best things and behave so beautifully when you try, you make me proud of you. I'm afraid to go alone. Do come and take care of me.

JO: You artful little puss.

AMY: I don't know what you mean.

JO: You wheedle and flatter your cross old sister to get your way. The idea of me being aristocratic and well-bred! The idea of you being afraid to go anywhere alone! I don't know which is the most absurd.

AMY: Jo...

JO: Oh very well, I'll go if I must and do my best. You shall command the expedition and I'll obey blindly. Will that satisfy you?

AMY: (*Kissing her.*) You're a perfect cherub. Now put on all your best things and I'll tell you how to behave at each place so that you make a good impression. I want people to like you.

JO: They never like me.

AMY: They would if you'd only try to be a little bit more agreeable. Do your hair the pretty way and put the pink rose in your bonnet. You look too sober in your plain suit. Take your light gloves and the embroidered handkerchief. We'll stop at Meg's and borrow her white sunshade – then you can have my dove-coloured one.

JO: You know I shall be perfectly miserable, don't you?

AMY: You'll be making me very happy. That should please your sense of duty.

JO: (*Ironic.*) Oh it does, it does!

AMY: One thing you do very well, Jo, is wear a shawl. I can't, but it's very nice to see you. Aunt March gave you that lovely one. Wear that.

JO: Yes, ma'am.

AMY: Is the point of my mantle in the middle and have I...? Are you teasing me?

JO: No. Just awaiting instructions.

AMY: We'll go to the Chesters first. They consider themselves very elegant, so I want you to put on your best deportment.

JO: (*Sashaying across the room.*) Like this?

AMY: (*Frustrated, almost in tears.*) Jo! Do behave properly or I shall never be able to go out in society again.

JO: (*Relenting.*) I will do exactly as I am bid.

AMY: Promise?

JO: Promise.

AMY: That's alright, then. Now, how do I look?

JO: Like a thing of beauty and a joy forever. You'd better come and help me change, dear. I'd hate to do the wrong thing. After all, visiting society is so very important!

They exit.

JANE EYRE

by Charlotte Bronte
dramatised by Shaun McKenna

See note on the dramatisation on page 18. JANE is 18, and has progressed from being a pupil at Lowood School to teaching there. Now she has decided to move on, and has placed an advertisement for a position. MISS TEMPLE, the headmistress of Lowood, a relatively young woman, is also about to leave – to be married.

MISS TEMPLE: Jane? Do you have an answer?

JANE: Yes. Today.

MISS TEMPLE: After all this time. I was beginning to think you would have to advertise again.

JANE: And I was determined not to. I dare not use up my little savings on rash speculation. I am a teacher here at Lowood and I should be grateful for my livelihood. And I was. But now that you are leaving, dear Maria...

MISS TEMPLE: I shall miss you.

JANE: And I you. (*Smiling.*) But you will be kept quite fully occupied, I imagine, in caring for your home and husband.

MISS TEMPLE: You're right, of course. I had come to believe those joys were never to be mine. They will be yours, too, one day.

JANE: I don't think so.

MISS TEMPLE: You are much too hard on yourself.

JANE: I have had reason.

MISS TEMPLE: But tell me about your letter. Is it a position?

JANE: Yes.

MISS TEMPLE: Where? What is the salary? When do you start? Oh Jane, I believe I am more excited than you are. How can you look so serious at a moment like this?

JANE: Because... because there is a world out there that holds the promise of every possibility, and that I know nothing about. It scares me and... yes, Maria, of course I am excited, more excited than I have ever been in my life.

MISS TEMPLE: But you seem so collected.

JANE: Do you know me so little?

MISS TEMPLE: You're not the angry little child I once held in my arms and rocked to sleep.

JANE: Yes, I am. Inside me. (*Changing the mood.*) And now I am to be a governess on thirty pounds a year.

MISS TEMPLE: That's fair.

JANE: A king's fortune to me, Maria. And only one child to look after, a girl, nine years old.

MISS TEMPLE: Where?

JANE: Somewhere called Thornfield hall, near Millcote in Yorkshire.

MISS TEMPLE: And your employer?

JANE: A Mrs Fairfax. Look, it is a crabbed hand, a little old-fashioned. I imagine her in a black gown and a widow's cap, an elderly lady, the model of English civility and respectability.

MISS TEMPLE: So your imagination has been racing, after all.

JANE: Yes, for I am entering a new servitude.

MISS TEMPLE: A new world.

JANE: Don't build my hopes too high. I don't want the picture in my head to be too enticing. Liberty, excitement, adventure – those are words that are too grand for me, it would be a waste of time for me to contemplate them. But a new servitude – oh yes, that's sweet enough.

MISS TEMPLE: And when do you start?

JANE: I haven't yet accepted the position.

MISS TEMPLE: But you will.

JANE: Oh yes. Yes, I will.

MISS TEMPLE: Let me embrace you, Jane. And let us remain friends.

JANE: Always.

They embrace.

FRAMLEY PARSONAGE

by Anthony Trollope

LADY LUFTON is a charming and sympathetic woman but has been horrified that her son has fallen in love with middle-class and impoverished LUCY ROBARTS, sister of LADY LUFTON's curate. She has demanded that LUCY refuse him. Now LUCY has been summoned to the house.

LADY LUFTON: Miss Robarts, I am much obliged to you for having come over to me here. You are, no doubt, aware of the subject I wish to discuss with you.

LUCY nods.

My son has spoken to me on the subject of – I think I understand, Miss Robarts, that there has been no engagement between you and him.

LUCY: None whatever. He made me an offer and I refused him.

LADY LUFTON: Oh. Then am I to understand that there is nothing now going on between you and my son? That the affair is over?

LUCY: That depends entirely upon you.

LADY LUFTON: On me?

LUCY: I do not know what your son has told you, Lady Lufton, but I would prefer that you and I have no secrets. Has he spoken to you about it?

LADY LUFTON: That is why I sent for you.

LUCY: And may I ask what he has told you? – I mean, as regards myself.

LADY LUFTON: (*A little put out by LUCY's direct manner.*) That he has made you an offer of marriage – a matter which is

very serious to me, as his mother. I thought I had better
see you and appeal to your good sense and judgement.

LUCY: Did he tell you my answer?

LADY LUFTON: Not in so many words. But you have just
said you refused him and I must express my admiration
for your good...

LUCY: Wait half a moment, Lady Lufton. Your son came
up to the parsonage and made me an offer, in person.
I refused him – and I am sorry for that, for I do love
him dearly. I did so for a mixture of reasons – a fear of
your displeasure amongst them. Then your son came
again, not to me but to my brother, and urged his suit
to him. Nothing can have been kinder to me than his
conduct, nothing more loving, more generous. At first
I thought, when he was speaking to me, that his feelings
were carrying him away. But when he came to see my
brother – I could not but believe that he had considered
it thoroughly and meant what he said. Can you
understand, Lady Lufton, that a girl placed as I am feels
ten times more assurance in that as in something that
seems to arise from the spur of the moment. I must tell
you that I love your son. I loved him from the first.
I was foolish enough to think that I could continue to
know him socially without loving him.

LADY LUFTON: I saw your feelings. That is why I took steps.

LUCY: Everybody saw my feelings. It was a matter of time
before I realised how strongly I loved him. It is no use
pretending I do not. I would stand at the altar with him
tomorrow and give him my hand...

LADY LUFTON: My dear Miss Robarts...

LUCY: Please hear me out. My brother asked me to agree
to see your son once more. If I saw him, I could not
have refused him.

LADY LUFTON: Well?

LUCY: I refused to see him. I was a coward. I could not
  endure to come into your house, as your son's wife, and
  be looked on coldly by you. Much as I love him,
  I cannot marry him if it will drive a wedge between
  mother and son.

LADY LUFTON: That is very...

LUCY: I have told your son that I will marry him when you
  ask me, not before.

  Pause.

LADY LUFTON: I am greatly struck by you, Miss Robarts.
  I now regard you with very different feelings from those
  I entertained when I left London.

LUCY: Thank you.

LADY LUFTON: You have behaved admirably in every way.

LUCY: Thank you.

LADY LUFTON: But, much as I like and admire your
  conduct, my strongest feelings in this matter must be
  those of a mother. I think such a marriage would be
  very – very ill-judged. My son is good-hearted, high
  principled and honest. But he is headstrong and he
  makes mistakes. I do not think an alliance with you
  would make either party happy.

LUCY: We need not argue about that. I have told you the
  only condition on which I shall accept him.

LADY LUFTON: I do not wish to argue, nor have you
  think me cruel in refusing my consent. I want you to
  believe that I am doing the best for my son.

LUCY: I am sure that you think you are; therefore no
  excuse is necessary. I think we have now said what we
  both wanted to say?

LADY LUFTON: I think we have. But I would like you to know how very highly I regard your conduct in this matter.

LUCY: I will wish you goodbye, then.

LADY LUFTON: Goodbye, Miss Robarts. Give my best love to Mrs Robarts and tell her that I shall hope to see her over here very soon. Perhaps you will all come over and dine.

LUCY: When your son is absent?

LADY LUFTON: Yes.

LUCY: I shall look forward to it.

RULING PASSIONS

by Shaun McKenna

See note on RULING PASSIONS on page 38. HENRIETTE DELUZY is a young governess, seen here with her 14 year old pupil, LOUISE DE PRASLIN, daughter of a French nobleman. LOUISE's mother is a difficult, unstable woman and HENRIETTE has taken it upon herself to provide the child with some emotional security. The scene is the schoolroom of the Praslin mansion in Paris, 1848.

A vase of irises and some fruit, artistically arranged, has been set out for LOUISE to draw. The clock chimes two. LOUISE is walking around the room with a pile of books on her head. She approaches the table and, in danger of losing the books, steps up onto a chair. She takes a deep breath.

HENRIETTE enters.

HENRIETTE: What on earth are you doing?

LOUISE: Sssh! I'm concentrating.

HENRIETTE: Louise!

LOUISE: I'm trying to climb onto the table with perfect posture.

HENRIETTE: I don't think there's an enormous demand for that in polite society, Louise.

LOUISE puts her finger to her lips, then steps onto the table in triumph.

Very nice. Now finish your drawing.

LOUISE: Mademoiselle!

She clambers down from the table, and sighs.

HENRIETTE: It's only a matter of practice.

LOUISE: I'll never be able to draw. I haven't got an eye.

HENRIETTE: Let me see.

LOUISE: (*Showing her.*) The irises look like pencils, the pencils like twigs and I'd rather not say what the fruit reminds me of.

HENRIETTE: Mmmm.

LOUISE: It's alright for Isabelle. Isabelle has an eye.

HENRIETTE: All well-bred young ladies draw.

LOUISE: Nobody's going to marry me just because I can draw irises. Can't I play the piano while everyone else draws? (*Considers a moment.*) Or they could draw me! I'd like that.

HENRIETTE: I'm sure you'll improve, with a little application.

LOUISE: You're not going to let me give it up, are you?

HENRIETTE smiles and shakes her head. She sits down beside her. LOUISE sighs.

HENRIETTE: Let's see what we can do.

LOUISE: Tear it up.

HENRIETTE: You have the perspective confused, that's all. You've made the jug too large and the bowl too small.

LOUISE: The jug is large.

HENRIETTE: Yes, but it's further away. Look.

She makes an adjustment with LOUISE's pencil.

See?

LOUISE: (*Dutifully.*) Yes. (*Seeing HENRIETTE's look.*) I do, I really do.

She draws for a moment.

What do you think of Charpentier?

HENRIETTE: What on earth do you mean?

LOUISE: Do you think he's handsome?

HENRIETTE: He is a servant.

LOUISE: (*With regret.*) Mmm. Mind you, my cousin's going to be a Count and he looks like a whippet. Isn't it funny?

HENRIETTE: Why did you ask the question?

LOUISE: Something my maid said.

HENRIETTE: You shouldn't listen to servants' gossip.

LOUISE: It wasn't gossip. She told me when she brought the note.

HENRIETTE: What note? You're full of... inconsequentialities today.

LOUISE: It's because I'm excited. The note was from Maman. She's taking me out for a drive in the Bois at three o'clock.

HENRIETTE: Lessons aren't over until four.

LOUISE: But Maman said...

HENRIETTE: Your mother should have asked me first.

LOUISE: You're not going to stop me, are you? Oh, say you won't stop me.

HENRIETTE: Louise...

LOUISE: I can't remember the last time I went out with Maman. All by myself.

HENRIETTE: Well...

LOUISE: I'll practice my drawing for a whole hour when I come back.

HENRIETTE: (*Relenting.*) Alright, then.

LOUISE: (*Excited.*) It's after two already. Does my hair need brushing? Am I smart enough? Which hat shall I wear? (*Seeing HENRIETTE's face.*) What's the matter?

HENRIETTE: Nothing.

LOUISE: We will have a wonderful time.

HENRIETTE: Of course you will. The boater with the green ribbon.

LOUISE: It makes me look a baby!

HENRIETTE: It makes you look charming.

LOUISE: You wouldn't make Isabelle wear a boater.

HENRIETTE: Isabelle is fifteen.

LOUISE: I am too, nearly. Alright. I won't argue. I'm too excited.

HENRIETTE: (*Sadly.*) Yes, I know.

LOUISE: Just Maman and me. Driving in the Bois.

HENRIETTE: (*Gently.*) Louise...

LOUISE: What?

HENRIETTE: If your mother should not... If she were to have one of her headaches... I don't want you to...

LOUISE: You think she won't come.

HENRIETTE: I didn't say that.

LOUISE: She'll come. I know she will. She must.

HENRIETTE: Yes, Louise. (*Tactfully.*) You must understand, Louise, your mother does not mean to...

LOUISE: Don't talk about her. You don't know anything about her.

HENRIETTE: Do you understand?

LOUISE: It doesn't matter.

HENRIETTE: Louise...

LOUISE: (*Shouting.*) It doesn't matter.

She runs out. HENRIETTE looks after her, concerned.

THE LAST CHRONICLE OF BARSET

by Anthony Trollope

GRACE CRAWLEY is 18, the daughter of an impoverished clergyman who has been accused of theft. She has been working at the kindly MISS PRETTYMAN's school, where she has been courted by the widowed MAJOR GRANTLY, whose influential parents are opposed to the match.

GRACE: Miss Prettyman, I have made up my mind that I will go home, if you please.

MISS PRETTYMAN: But why? This is your home now.

GRACE: I think I should be with mamma just at present.

MISS PRETTYMAN: Your mamma has your sister with her.

GRACE: Yes. Jane is there.

MISS PRETTYMAN: Then, my dear... If that is the only reason... Of course, your mamma would like to have you always near her, unless you are married, but there are reasons why this should not be so.

GRACE: Of course there are.

MISS PRETTYMAN: I cannot think there is any good ground for leaving us now – just now.

GRACE: It is because of papa, and this charge.

MISS PRETTYMAN: But Grace...

GRACE: I think I know what you are going to say, Miss Prettyman.

MISS PRETTYMAN: Then let me say it.

GRACE: But please hear me for a moment first. I beg your pardon, Miss Prettyman, I do indeed, but I must go home and I know I should. We are all disgraced. The police are to take him to court on Thursday, here in Silverbridge, and everyone will know it. It cannot be right for me to go on teaching here while it is going on. I won't. I can't, Miss Prettyman. I don't know what I am saying half the time, my mind is so distracted. (*Almost in tears.*) And I will bring disgrace on your school.

MISS PRETTYMAN: Are there any other reasons?

GRACE: I don't know.

MISS PRETTYMAN: But I know. I know them all, very well. And I think you should stay.

GRACE: I cannot.

MISS PRETTYMAN: To me, the reasons you give for going are the reasons you should stay.

GRACE: I'm very grateful, but I cannot have the girls looking at me, and whispering, and wondering.

MISS PRETTYMAN: Come here, my love. (*Putting her arms around her.*) Grace, do you not know that I love you dearly? I love you as if you were my own, and you must trust that I know what is best for you.

GRACE: I must go home.

MISS PRETTYMAN: And you shall, if you think it right at last. But let us talk first. Nobody here, you know, has the slightest suspicion that your father has done anything that is in the least dishonest.

GRACE: I know that. But the servants...

MISS PRETTYMAN: If the servants say anything to offend you, I shall...

GRACE: They don't say anything. But they look. I had better go home.

MISS PRETTYMAN: Don't you think your mother is burdened enough without another mouth to feed. Have you thought of that.

GRACE: Yes.

MISS PRETTYMAN: As for the work, if you stay you shall not be burdened with teaching. I have some old papers that want copying and settling. You may sit here and do that for employment.

GRACE: No, no. I must go home.

MISS PRETTYMAN: And what of Major Grantly?

GRACE: What of him?

MISS PRETTYMAN: He loves you.

GRACE: With my father's name disgraced I must think no more of Major Grantly.

MISS PRETTYMAN: He has been to see me.

GRACE: When?

MISS PRETTYMAN: Yesterday. When the news broke of your father's – trouble. He asked my permission to have an interview with you. I told him you were not up to it at present. Did I do wrong?

GRACE: No. That was very kind. Thank you.

MISS PRETTYMAN: He behaved in the most gentleman-like manner imaginable.

GRACE: I am sure he did. But it changes nothing. I must go.

MISS PRETTYMAN: I am asking you, Grace, as a favour to me who loves you, not to go. At least consider the matter further.

GRACE: I...

MISS PRETTYMAN: At least consider.

Pause.

GRACE: Very well. I will think about it. May I go to my room, now? I have a dreadful headache.

MISS PRETTYMAN: Of course. (*As she goes.*) You will do the right thing, Grace. I know you will.

EIGHT COUSINS
or THE AUNT HILL

by Louisa May Alcott

ROSE, a 14 year old orphan, has made her home with an eccentric but kindly uncle. She has previously met a local girl, ANNABEL BLISS, and disliked her. ROSE has sprained her ankle and ANNABEL takes the opportunity to visit. The novel is set in America in the 1860s. ANNABEL has just been shown in to ROSE's room by the maid.

ANNABEL: How nice to have a maid. Still, dear, you must be very lonely and feel the need of a bosom friend.

ROSE: I have my cousins.

ANNABEL: Gracious, child! You don't make friends with those great boys, do you? Mamma says she really doesn't think it's proper for you to be with them so much.

ROSE: (*Offended.*) They're like brothers – and my aunts do think it's proper.

ANNABEL: I was going to say I should be glad to have you for my bosom friend, for Hatty Mason and I have had an awful quarrel and don't speak. She is too mean to live, so I gave her up. Just think, she never paid back one of the caramels I've given her, and she never invited me to her party. I could have forgiven the caramels but to be left out in that rude way was more than I could bear and I told her never to look at me again as long as she lived.

ROSE: You're very kind but I don't think I want a bosom friend, thank you.

Offended, ANNABEL picks up a book from the table.

ANNABEL: You're studying French, I see. Who's your teacher?

ROSE: I don't study it. I read it as well as English and uncle and I often speak it for hours. He talks like a native and says I have a remarkably good accent.

ANNABEL: Oh, indeed?

ROSE: I'll be going abroad with uncle in a year or two and he knows how important it is to understand the languages. Half the girls who leave school can't speak decent French and when they go abroad they are so mortified. I shall be very glad to help you, if you like, for of course you have no one to talk with at home.

ANNABEL: Thank you, dear, I don't need any help, for our teacher is from Paris and of course he speaks better French than your uncle.

Pause, while they both draw up new battle lines.

Do you like my new ear-rings? Papa gave them to me last week and everyone says they are lovely.

ROSE: (*Looking at them, in genuine admiration.*) Oh, they are lovely. If only Uncle would let me wear ear-rings I should be perfectly happy.

ANNABEL: Don't mind your uncle. Papa laughed at me at first but he likes them now and says I shall have diamond solitaires when I am eighteen.

ROSE: I've got a pair of those now – they were Mamma's – and a beautiful pair of turquoise and pearl ones that I'm dying to wear.

ANNABEL: Then do it. I'll pierce your ears for you. You wear a bit of silk in them till they are well. Your hair will hide them nicely and then, one day, slip in your smallest ear-rings and see if your uncle doesn't like them.

ROSE: I asked him once whether piercing my ears wouldn't make my eyes better. They were rather red, you see, and I heard somewhere that it does make your eyes better.

ANNABEL: It's well known. And your eyes are rather red at the moment, aren't they?

ROSE: Are they?

ANNABEL: Oh yes. I'd better pierce your ears before they get any worse. Where's your sewing box?

ROSE: Does it hurt much?

ANNABEL: Oh no. Just a prick and a pull and it's all over. Pull up your hair and give me a big needle.

ROSE: I really think I should ask Uncle's permission first.

ANNABEL: Has he ever forbidden it?

ROSE: No. We've never mentioned it.

ANNABEL: There you are, then.

Taking needle and thread from ROSE's sewing box.

Unless, of course, you're scared.

ROSE: Certainly not.

ANNABEL: (*Needle poised.*) Say 'Punch' when you're ready.

ROSE: (*After a moment.*) Punch! Ow!

ANNABEL: Other side.

ROSE: Punch! Ow!

ANNABEL: Oh Rose, did I hurt you?

ROSE: (*Through tears of pain.*) No. Not at all.

ANNABEL: Well, just pull the bits of silk often and cold cream your ears every night and you'll soon be ready for the rings. What's the matter?

ROSE: Nothing.

ANNABEL: We'll have to be bosom friends now. I've drawn your blood. We'll be bosom friends forever.

ROSE: (*Appalled.*) Oh dear.

GREAT EXPECTATIONS

by Charles Dickens

PIP, a young man, is an orphan who has had his life transformed by the financial generosity of an unknown benefactor. He has returned to the marshy Kent landscape of his childhood, thinking he is to meet his benefactor at last. Instead he is attacked, tied up and confronted by ORLICK, who bears a grudge against him. ORLICK had been an apprentice in the forge of blacksmith JOE GARGERY, who brought up PIP as a child. ORLICK was attracted to BIDDY, who went on to marry GARGERY after the death of his wife, PIP's sister. In this scene, PIP is tied to a chair while ORLICK gloats.

ORLICK: Now I've got you!

PIP: Unbind me! Let me go!

ORLICK: Don't you worry. I'll let you go alright. I'll let you go to the moon. I'll let you go to the stars! All in good time.

PIP: What is this about? Why have you lured me here?

ORLICK: Don't you know?

PIP: Why did you set upon me in the dark?

ORLICK: Because I mean to do it all myself. One keeps a secret better than two.

PIP: But what have I done?

ORLICK: You've been my enemy, that's what you've done.

PIP: I swear I...

ORLICK: (*Hitting him.*) Shut your trap! (*Picking up a pistol.*) Recognise this?

PIP: No.

ORLICK: (*Hitting him again.*) I'm not playing games, you know. You recognise this pistol?

PIP: Yes.

ORLICK: Where did you see it before?

PIP: At Gargery's forge.

ORLICK: Where I had my place. Where I had my Biddy.

PIP: She was never 'your' Biddy.

ORLICK: You cost me that place. You did. You cost me my Biddy.

PIP: No. You are quite mistaken in that.

ORLICK: You cost me my Biddy. You blackened my name, ruined my reputation.

PIP: You managed that all by yourself.

ORLICK: No.

PIP: How could I have blackened your reputation if you hadn't shown yourself to be... the kind of man you are?

ORLICK: You're a liar. You'll use any means, and spend any money, to drive me out of this part of the world, won't you? Well, let me tell you something. By the time tonight is done with, you'll wish you *had* driven me out.

PIP: What are you going to do to me?

ORLICK: I'm going to have your life.

Pause. Then PIP starts to yell.

PIP: (*Yelling.*) Help! Help! Someone help me!

ORLICK: You was always in my way, ever since you was a child. Well, this present night you'll go out of my way. You'll be dead.

PIP: Help! Help!

ORLICK: It's no good yelling. There's nobody to hear. Yes, you'll be dead. And more than that, there won't be a rag of you left. Not a rag of you, not a bone of you left on earth. You know where we are?

PIP: Let me out. I'm rich, I can pay you...

ORLICK: We're by the lime pits. That's where we are. And when you've once been through the lime kiln, there'll be nothing left. Not a scrap.

He swigs from a bottle.

PIP: You won't do it.

ORLICK: Oh won't I? Who do you think got rid of that shrew sister of yours?

PIP: It was you!

ORLICK: Oh yes, it was me as did the killin'. But the fault was yours.

PIP: You villain.

ORLICK: I come up on her from behind, as I come upon you tonight. I give it her. I left her for dead, and if there'd been a limekiln as nigh her as there is now nigh you, she shouldn't have survived as long as she did. But it wasn't me as did it; it was you.

PIP: What are you talking about?

ORLICK: You was favoured and I was bullied. I was bullied and beat and you got off scot free. Now you pays for it. You done it, and now you pays for it.

PIP: You're mad.

ORLICK: Maybe I am. Maybe I'm mad. Ain't it funny. I'm mad – and you're as good as dead.

TO SERVE THEM ALL MY DAYS

by R.F. Delderfield
dramatised by Shaun McKenna

See note on the play on page 12. DAVY POWLETT-JONES,
a young schoolteacher, has lost his wife, and one of his twin
baby girls, in a tragic accident. His other daughter, GRACE,
is seriously ill in hospital. Here he is visited in his rooms by
a 16 year old pupil, CHAD BOYER.

*DAVY's room. He sits, in his dressing gown, at a desk piled high
with papers. BOYER knocks at the door.*

DAVY: Come in.

BOYER: Am I disturbing you?

DAVY: God knows I could do with the company. Sit down,
Chad. You can stay till Silence Bell.

BOYER: Thanks. (*Holding out two books.*) I bought you these.
I remember you quoting from them in the Upper Fifth
last year. You said you'd had them both out there during
the war but lost them with the rest of your kit at Third
Ypres. Here.

DAVY: (*Touched, taking the books.*) That was a nice thought,
Chad. Thank you. I don't think many would have had it.

BOYER: I found them on Charing Cross Road during the
hols, sir. I was going to keep them as a leaving souvenir,
but... I thought perhaps you could do with a couple of
old friends just now.

DAVY: (*Moved.*) Thank you. (*After a moment.*) Can I tell you
something?

BOYER: Yes.

DAVY: (*Indicating the books.*) They were a comfort to me
during the war... No, 'comfort' is the wrong word. They

had a personal message. They kept me going. Maybe they'll work again. I'll treasure them.

Pause.

BOYER: Sir?

DAVY: Yes, Chad?

BOYER: Well... it's a bit awkward, really. The other chaps wanted me to tell you how they felt, sir, about... We all liked Mrs Powlett-Jones. I know talking doesn't do a damn... doesn't help, sir, but... they wanted you to know.

DAVY: Thank you.

BOYER: How's Grace?

DAVY: It'll take months for the bones to knit together. But she'll survive. It's me I'm not so sure about.

BOYER: Oh, come on, sir.

DAVY: This is going to take some weathering, Chad. Frankly, I can't see myself making it.

BOYER: That's daft.

DAVY: Oh, I don't mean I'm going to cut my throat. Just... I need to get away from here.

BOYER: That's daft too. I'm sorry, sir, but it's just not you at all. We need you here.

DAVY: Would you mind telling me why? The way you might discuss it with Dobson, or some other boy. I don't know if I'm going to stay on, but if I am, I need to know why.

BOYER: But that's... You have to stay on.

DAVY: I don't think I can. This was our home.

BOYER: But you must. Look, this isn't flannel, sir. You belong here. You have from the first day. It isn't because the chaps like you either – they do, of course, I didn't mean... But you... you get through to people, the way other masters can't. You make it mean something.

DAVY: Can't I do that somewhere else.

BOYER: Not like you can here. You learned the trick of it here. You're part of the place, just like Algy... the head, I mean. I never gave a damn about history before you taught it.

DAVY: (*Bitter, flicking papers on his desk.*) History.

BOYER: Maybe I'm talking a lot of coc... of rubbish, sir, but I don't think so.

Pause. A bell rings distantly.

BOYER: There's the Silence bell. (*Standing.*) I have to check the junior dorm.

DAVY nods. BOYER makes for the door.

(*Stopping in the door.*) You belong here, sir.

DAVY: (*Sharp.*) I get the message, Chad.

BOYER: You'll think about it?

DAVY: I'll think about it.

BOYER goes. DAVY stares out front, lost.

THERESE RAQUIN

by Emile Zola

LAURENT, an amateur artist, has murdered CAMILLE RAQUIN for love of his wife, THERESE RAQUIN. Now he has married THERESE but both are so racked with guilt that their relationship is deeply unhappy. LAURENT has met a friend of the Raquin family, a rather old-maidish elderly man named GRIVET, and has taken him back to see his recent work. The scene is in LAURENT's studio. There are a number of canvases stacked against a table.

LAURENT: I'm very grateful to you for taking the time. I'm so pleased I met you. Since I left the railway, life has been a bit...

GRIVET: I understand. It's natural you should lack intellectual stimulation surrounded by a pack of women.

LAURENT: It's not that. I'm not home much. I spend my time here, painting.

GRIVET: (*Eyeing the stack of canvases.*) You're certainly prolific. How pleasant to have so much leisure.

LAURENT: Leisure? I've been working hard, I assure you.

GRIVET: So it would appear.

An awkward pause.

LAURENT: Can I offer you something? There's some brandy somewhere.

GRIVET: No, no. I really don't have time.

LAURENT: Sorry. What am I thinking of? It's just nice to... Look, Monsieur Grivet, you never had much of an opinion of my painting, did you?

GRIVET: Really, what a question.

LAURENT: Please be frank. What are old friends for, after all?

This description rather surprises GRIVET.

GRIVET: Well... I'm not an expert but...

LAURENT: But you know what you like, eh?

GRIVET: Are you laughing at me?

LAURENT: No, no. But, please, I need an outside eye. Here.

He spreads the canvases out in front of GRIVET.

They're only studies, of course. I'm planning a big picture. I know it's a bit ambitious to start off with but my head is bursting with ideas and images and I...

He falls silent as he watches GRIVET's face.

GRIVET: (*After a moment.*) These are all yours?

LAURENT: As bad as that?

With a gesture, GRIVET silences him and stares intently at two or more of the canvases.

GRIVET: You're not lying to me?

LAURENT: (*Offended.*) Monsieur Grivet, please.

GRIVET: Frankly, I find it difficult to believe.

LAURENT: They are all mine.

GRIVET: Then, my dear fellow, something of a miracle has occurred. I never imagined you had talent like this in you.

LAURENT: You really like them?

GRIVET: They're not sophisticated, of course, but such life. Such energy. They are wonderfully exciting.

LAURENT: I don't know how to thank you, sir. Of course, I knew they were different to my other stuff, but... You really think they're good?

GRIVET: First rate.

LAURENT: Thank you.

GRIVET: I've only one... an observation more than a criticism, if you don't mind my saying.

LAURENT: Not at all. Go ahead.

GRIVET: It's simply that all these studies have a likeness. Not that they're the same, but there's a sort of... as if they were all from one family. Yes, that's it. Even the women have something – violent – about them, as though they were men in disguise. If you're going to make one big picture from them, you must alter a few of the faces.

LAURENT: I don't quite see...

GRIVET: You can't have them all brothers. People would laugh.

LAURENT stares at the canvases in mounting horror. GRIVET takes out his watch.

It's almost seven. I should be in Montparnasse. Excuse me, won't you?

LAURENT: (*Still gazing at the pictures.*) Of course.

GRIVET: Congratulations, my dear fellow. Won't your pretty wife be pleased when your work is hanging in the Academy?

LAURENT: (*Shaking hands.*) Goodbye, Monsieur Grivet. And thanks again.

GRIVET exits. LAURENT turns back and starts to rifle through other canvases, with mounting frenzy. Finally, the conclusion is inescapable.

Camille! They're all Camille!

THE POSTMAN ALWAYS RINGS TWICE

by James M. Cain
dramatised by Shaun McKenna

See note on the dramatisation on page 25. CORA and FRANK have murdered CORA's husband, NICK PAPADAKIS. Their slimy lawyer organised a clever manoeuver to get them off. As a result of this, CORA's signed confession is in the lawyer's safe. KENNEDY once worked for the lawyer and has now turned up in the lunch-room owned and run by FRANK and CORA.

KENNEDY: Hello there.

FRANK: I'm sorry, mister, we're closing early tonight. I should have locked up already... Hey, it's Kennedy, right?

KENNEDY: You remember.

FRANK: 'Course I remember. From Katz's office. How is Katz?

KENNEDY: No idea. We had a little argument and I walked out. Is there any coffee?

FRANK: (*Ill at ease.*) Sure. Sit down.

KENNEDY sits. FRANK pours.

What are you doing now?

KENNEDY: Not a thing. Fact of the matter, that's why I wanted to see you. I was wondering if you could maybe let me have a little money.

FRANK: I guess. You did us a good turn back there. I don't keep much around but if fifty or sixty bucks would help...

KENNEDY: I was hoping you could make it more.

Pause.

FRANK: OK, Kennedy. What is this?

KENNEDY: The paper, the one I wrote up for Mrs Papadakis, that was still in the files when I left. I thought maybe you'd like to get it back.

FRANK: (*Laughing awkwardly.*) You mean that hop dream she called a confession?

KENNEDY: That's the one. Of course, I know there's nothing in it, but I thought, for you, it might have... sentimental value.

FRANK: How much?

KENNEDY: How much would you give?

FRANK: Like you said, there's nothing in it. I might give a hundred.

KENNEDY: I figured more.

FRANK: Yeah?

KENNEDY: I figured twenty-five grand.

FRANK: Are you crazy?

KENNEDY: You got ten grand from Katz. This place has been making money, maybe five grand. And you could get ten from the bank on the property. That's twenty-five grand.

FRANK: You'd strip me clean for that worthless bit of paper?

KENNEDY: I don't think the D.A. would think it was worthless.

FRANK: Get out of here.

FRANK moves to attack KENNEDY. KENNEDY draws a gun.

KENNEDY: I'm not going anywhere.

FRANK: Put that away.

KENNEDY: Not a chance.

FRANK: (*After a moment.*) I guess you got me.

KENNEDY: I guess so.

FRANK: But you're figuring way too high. We got ten from Katz, that's true, and we made five off the place, but we spent a grand in the last couple of weeks. We both took trips. And we can't get ten on the property. Things the way they are, we'd be lucky to get five. Maybe we could get four.

KENNEDY: Keep talking.

FRANK: Ten, four and four. That makes eighteen.

Pause.

KENNEDY: Alright. Eighteen thousand dollars.

FRANK: If you look behind you, Kennedy, I think you'll find my wife has a gun pointed straight at your head.

KENNEDY: You think I'm gonna fall for that?

FRANK: I'm just letting you know, Kennedy. If you don't turn round, she'll blow your head away. If you do turn round, I'm gonna break your goddamn neck.

What's it to be, Kennedy?

LE GRAND MEAULNES

by Alain-Fournier

AUGUSTIN MEAULNES, a charismatic 15 year old schoolboy, has had an extraordinary adventure in a place he calls 'The Enchanted Château'. He does not know how to get back there, but has some clues. His friend and colleague, FRANÇOIS SEUREL, is a year younger and has a crippled foot. FRANÇOIS is the schoolteacher's son. Here, they are trying to reconstruct a map to the Château.

MEAULNES: (*With the map.*) It has to be somewhere in this triangle.

FRANÇOIS: You don't know where it is.

MEAULNES: Do you want to help or not?

FRANÇOIS: Of course I do.

MEAULNES: Then stop arguing with everything I say.

FRANÇOIS: I'm only trying to make you see...

MEAULNES: See what? That I'm imagining things?

FRANÇOIS: No.

MEAULNES: I knew you didn't believe me.

FRANÇOIS: I do believe you.

MEAULNES: Then why are you trying to stop me?

FRANÇOIS: Because if you go off again, searching for this Enchanted Château, as you call it, and something happens to you, how do you think I'll feel?

MEAULNES: (*After a moment.*) Then you do believe me?

FRANÇOIS: I believe you fell asleep on the road. I believe the pony went astray. I believe you found somewhere. Somewhere special. And I believe...

MEAULNES: Yes?

FRANÇOIS: I believe you met a beautiful girl and want to find her again.

MEAULNES: Yvonne de Galais. Her name was Yvonne de Galais.

FRANÇOIS: You never told me that.

MEAULNES: (*Evasive.*) Didn't I?

FRANÇOIS: No, you didn't. That's the key to it all, don't you see? If you know her name and you know she lives in a château, what are you worrying about. Even if the pony went astray by fifty miles, there can't be that many châteaux. All you have to do is match the name to the place. Ask someone. Somebody will have heard of the Galais family.

MEAULNES: What if it wasn't her real name?

FRANÇOIS: Why shouldn't it be?

MEAULNES: I don't know. But just suppose.

FRANÇOIS: It's the best clue we have. If you don't ask around, I will.

MEAULNES: No. Don't.

FRANÇOIS: You're not being sensible, Augustin.

MEAULNES: What I saw at the Château wasn't sensible. What I feel about Yvonne isn't sensible. I'm starting to wonder if I dreamed it all.

FRANÇOIS: When I said that, I thought you were going to hit me.

MEAULNES: It was so real. The music, the dancing, the lights, the food... all solid, all absolutely real. And yet – even when I was there it felt impossible, like someone had cast a spell on the place, on the people there, on me... And now I'm back here, where everything is ordinary and everyday and commonplace and... I can't bear it, François. I have to go back. I have to find it again. It has to be like it was.

Pause.

FRANÇOIS: You're going, then?

MEAULNES: When I find enough clues. Yes, I'm going.

FRANÇOIS: Oh.

Pause.

MEAULNES: Why don't you come with me?

FRANÇOIS: I can't.

MEAULNES: You can do anything you want if you put your mind to it.

FRANÇOIS: My father would be too upset.

MEAULNES: He'd get over it. People can get over anything.

FRANÇOIS: You haven't got over meeting Yvonne de Galais.

MEAULNES: (*After a moment.*) No. No, I haven't.

FRANÇOIS: Anyway we'd probably end up walking miles and I'd hold you back.

MEAULNES: Come with me.

FRANÇOIS: Your Yvonne won't want to meet a cripple.

MEAULNES: Come with me.

FRANÇOIS: It's too dangerous.

MEAULNES: Come with me.

Pause.

FRANÇOIS: Alright. I'll go with you.

TOM SAWYER

by Mark Twain

TOM SAWYER and HUCKLEBERRY FINN are teenage boys, in nineteenth century America. They are digging for treasure.

TOM: I like this.

HUCK: So do I.

TOM: If we find a treasure here, what are you going to do with your share?

HUCK: I'll have a pie and a glass of soda every day and I'll go to every circus that comes along. I'll have a fine old time.

TOM: Aren't you going to save any of it?

HUCK: Save it? What for?

TOM: To have something to live on by-and-by.

HUCK: Oh, that ain't any use. Pap would come back to this town some day and get his claws on it if I didn't hurry up. He'd clean it out pretty quick. What you going to with yours, Tom?

TOM: I'm going to buy a new drum, and a sure 'nough sword, and a red necktie, and a bull-pup, and get married.

HUCK: Married?

TOM: That's it.

HUCK: Tom, you – you ain't in your right mind.

TOM: You'll see.

HUCK: That's the foolishest thing you could do, Tom. Look at Pap and my mother. Fight! Why they used to fight all the time. I remember, mighty well.

TOM: The girl I'm going to marry won't fight.

HUCK: Tom, I reckon they're all alike. They'll all comb you. You'd better think about this awhile. I tell you, you'd better. What's the name of this gal?

TOM: I'll tell you some time. Not now.

HUCK: Alright, that'll do. Only if you get married I'll be lonesomer than ever.

TOM: No you won't, you'll come and live with me. Now, stir out of this, and get digging.

They dig.

HUCK: Do they always bury treasure as deep as this?

TOM: Sometimes. Not always. Not generally. I reckon we haven't got the right place.

HUCK: Where shall we dig next?

TOM: I reckon maybe we'll tackle the old tree that's over yonder on Cardiff Hill, back of the widow's.

HUCK: But, if we find treasure – won't the widow take it away from us? It'll be on her land.

TOM: Just let her try it. Whoever finds one of these hid treasures, it belongs to him. Don't make no difference whose land it's on.

HUCK: You sure, Tom? And you sure we're in the wrong place here? Couldn't it be something else?

TOM: Like what?

HUCK: I don't know. Maybe, sometimes witches interfere. Maybe that's what's the trouble now.

TOM: Shucks! Witches ain't got no power in the daylight.

HUCK: Well, that's so. I didn't think of that.

TOM: I know what the matter is!

HUCK: Yes, Tom?

TOM: What a blamed lot of fools we are. You got to find out where the shadow of the limb falls at midnight, and that's where you dig.

HUCK: Then confound it, we've fooled away all this work for nothing. Now hang it all, we got to come back in the night. It's an awful long way.

TOM: Can you get out at night?

HUCK: I bet I will. We got to do it tonight, too, because if somebody sees these holes they'll know in a minute what's here and they'll go for it.

TOM: Well, I'll come and meow outside your window tonight.

HUCK: Alright. Let's hide these tools in the bushes.

STRANGE MEETING

by Susan Hill

HILLIARD and BARTON are young officers, in the trenches during World War I. HILLIARD is the more experienced, having already been wounded and hospitalised. The open, friendly eagerness of BARTON has helped to bring him out of the deep depression his wartime experiences had engendered. The two have become very close. Now BARTON is suffering, appalled by the waste and by the horror of war.

BARTON: What is happening to me?

HILLIARD: You haven't stopped feeling. You've just told me as much.

BARTON: That boy...

HILLIARD: You can't feel every man's death completely and all of the time, David, you simply cannot.

BARTON: Every man's death diminishes me.

HILLIARD: Yes. So you have just told me the truth, haven't you?

BARTON: Have I?

HILLIARD: That you are diminished and know as much. And you are changed. And ashamed. That you feel it. Some people would scarcely have noticed how many men were killed, they've gone past it. It's all become part of the day's work.

BARTON: What kind of men are those?

HILLIARD: Precisely. But all the same, you know as well as I do that if you are here and doing this job, you have to shove things out of the way all the time. We'd never carry on at all otherwise.

BARTON: Then I wonder if we ought to 'carry on' at all.

HILLIARD: If you truly believe that you can go and say so to Garrett tomorrow, register as a conscientious objector – lay down your arms. I imagine it would be hard – it was hard enough for your brother and he hadn't gone through the business of joining up and serving. But if that is what you feel, then you must do it.

BARTON: It would be funk, wouldn't it? I went through all that before I came out here. It would be funk.

HILLIARD: You hadn't seen anything then.

BARTON: All the more reason why it would be funk and seen to be so.

HILLIARD: Are you afraid of what else is to come?

BARTON: I'm afraid of myself. Of what I am becoming, of what it will do to me.

HILLIARD: Are you afraid of your own dying?

BARTON: Oh no. I've thought about that too. No. I have never really been afraid of that.

HILLIARD: 'It's a brave act of valour to condemn death, but where life is more terrible, it is the truest valour to live.'

BARTON: Is that true?

HILLIARD: It isn't going to get any better. It's not going to stop being more terrible. None of that nonsense about its all being over and done with by Christmas, about our driving them out like foxes from cover. I scarcely believe that it will ever be over. At any rate there is no point in thinking so.

BARTON: I asked you if it were true that where life is more terrible it is the truest valour to live.

HILLIARD: Isn't it something you have to make up your own mind about?

BARTON: Is it true for you, then?

HILLIARD: (*After a moment.*) Yes, it's true. I think so. And you?

BARTON: I don't know. (*Breaking the mood.*) What a philosophical night.

HILLIARD: No. We've been talking about what is happening, about yesterday, today and tomorrow. It's going to be bloody wet and bloody cold. Come on.

He gets up to go.

BARTON: I love you, Hilliard.

Pause. HILLIARD looks at him, and smiles.

HILLIARD: Yes.

He goes.

This adaptation published by permission of the author. *Strange Meeting* is published by Hamish Hamilton © Susan Hill 1971, 1989.